TABLE OF CONTENTS

INTRODUCTION/WELCOME

WELCOME FROM
CHRYSLER GROUP LLC . . . .

CONTROLS AT A GLANCE

DRIVER COCKPIT 6
INSTRUMENT CLUSTER 8

GETTING STARTED

KEY FOB 10
KEYLESS ENTER-N-GO™ 11
REMOTE START 12
THEFT ALARM 13
SEAT BELT 13
SUPPLEMENTAL RESTRAINT SYSTEM
(SRS) — AIR BAGS 14
CHILD RESTRAINTS 15
FRONT SEATS 20
HEATED/VENTILATED SEATS 22
HEATED STEERING WHEEL 23
TILT STEERING COLUMN 24

OPERATING YOUR VEHICLE

ENGINE BREAK-IN
RECOMMENDATIONS 25
DIESEL ENGINE BREAK-IN
RECOMMENDATIONS 25
TURN SIGNALS/WIPER/WASHER/HIGH
BEAMS LEVER 25
HEADLIGHT SWITCH 26
SPEED CONTROL 27
EIGHT–SPEED AUTOMATIC TRANSMISSION
— IF EQUIPPED 29
ELECTRONIC RANGE SELECT (ERS)
OPERATION 29
ELECTRONIC RANGE SELECT (ERS)
OPERATION – 8 SPEED
TRANSMISSION 31
AIR SUSPENSION SYSTEM 31
MANUAL CLIMATE CONTROLS WITHOUT
TOUCH-SCREEN 33
MANUAL CLIMATE CONTROLS WITH
TOUCH-SCREEN 34
AUTOMATIC CLIMATE CONTROLS WITH
TOUCH-SCREEN 36
PARKSENSE® REAR PARK ASSIST . . . 37
PARKVIEW® REAR BACK-UP CAMERA . 38
TIRE PRESSURE MONITOR SYSTEM
(TPMS) – 2500 MODELS ONLY 38
POWER SLIDING REAR WINDOW 39
POWER SUNROOF 40
WIND BUFFETING 41

ELECTRONICS

YOUR VEHICLE'S SOUND SYSTEM . . . 42
IDENTIFYING YOUR RADIO 44
Uconnect® Access (AVAILABLE ON
Uconnect® 8.4A AND Uconnect® 8.4AN)
(IF EQUIPPED) 45

. . . 54
. . . 57
. . . 63
. . . 82

. . . 101
ELECTRONIC VEHICLE INFORMATION
CENTER (EVIC) 101
PROGRAMMABLE FEATURES 102
UNIVERSAL GARAGE DOOR OPENER
(HomeLink®) 104
POWER INVERTER 107
POWER OUTLETS 108

OFF-ROAD CAPABILITIES

FOUR WHEEL DRIVE OPERATION . . . 109

UTILITY

TONNEAU COVER 112
EASY-OFF TAILGATE 112
PICKUP BOX 113
RAMBOX® 114
TOWING & PAYLOAD 118
TOW/HAUL MODE 120
INTEGRATED TRAILER BRAKE
MODULE 120
RECREATIONAL TOWING (BEHIND
MOTORHOME, ETC.) 121

DIESEL

DIESEL ENGINE BREAK-IN
RECOMMENDATIONS 124
DIESEL ENGINE STARTING
PROCEDURES 124
DIESEL EXHAUST BRAKE (ENGINE
BRAKING) 125
IDLE-UP FEATURE (AUTOMATIC
TRANSMISSION ONLY) 126
ENGINE MOUNTED FUEL FILTER/WATER
SEPARATOR 127
UNDERBODY MOUNTED FUEL
FILTER/WATER SEPARATOR 128
ADDING FUEL – DIESEL ENGINE
ONLY 129
EXHAUST REGENERATION 129
COOL-DOWN IDLE CHART 131
DIESEL EXHAUST FLUID 131

WHAT TO DO IN EMERGENCIES

ROADSIDE ASSISTANCE 134
INSTRUMENT CLUSTER WARNING
LIGHTS 134
IF YOUR ENGINE OVERHEATS 138
JACKING AND TIRE CHANGING 138
JUMP-STARTING 152
EMERGENCY TOW HOOKS 154
SHIFT LEVER OVERRIDE 154
TOWING A DISABLED VEHICLE 157
FREEING A STUCK VEHICLE 158
EVENT DATA RECORDER (EDR) 159

D0939857

TABLE OF CONTENTS

MAINTAINING YOUR VEHICLE

OPENING THE HOOD 160
ENGINE COMPARTMENT 161
FLUIDS AND CAPACITIES 166
MAINTENANCE SCHEDULE – GASOLINE
ENGINE 171
MAINTENANCE SCHEDULE – DIESEL
ENGINE 176
FUSES 181
TIRE PRESSURES 185
WHEEL AND WHEEL TRIM CARE . . . 186
EXTERIOR BULBS 187

CUSTOMER ASSISTANCE

CHRYSLER GROUP LLC CUSTOMER
CENTER 188

CHRYSLER CANADA INC. CUSTOMER
CENTER 188
ASSISTANCE FOR THE HEARING
IMPAIRED 188
PUBLICATIONS ORDERING 188
REPORTING SAFETY DEFECTS IN THE
50 UNITED STATES AND
WASHINGTON, D.C. 189

MOPAR ACCESSORIES

AUTHENTIC ACCESSORIES BY
MOPAR® 190

INDEX 191

FAQ (How To?) 194
FREQUENTLY ASKED QUESTIONS . . . 194

INTRODUCTION/WELCOME

WELCOME FROM CHRYSLER GROUP LLC

Congratulations on selecting your new Chrysler Group LLC vehicle. Be assured that it represents precision workmanship, distinctive styling, and high quality - all essentials that are traditional to our vehicles.

Your new Chrysler Group LLC vehicle has characteristics to enhance the driver's control under some driving conditions. These are to assist the driver and are never a substitute for attentive driving. They can never take the driver's place. Always drive carefully.

Your new vehicle has many features for the comfort and convenience of you and your passengers. Some of these should not be used when driving because they take your eyes from the road or your attention from driving. Never text while driving or take your eyes more than momentarily off the road.

This guide illustrates and describes the operation of features and equipment that are either standard or optional on this vehicle. This guide may also include a description of features and equipment that are no longer available or were not ordered on this vehicle. Please disregard any features and equipment described in this guide that are not available on this vehicle. Chrysler Group LLC reserves the right to make changes in design and specifications and/or make additions to or improvements to its products without imposing any obligation upon itself to install them on products previously manufactured.

This User Guide has been prepared to help you quickly become acquainted with the important features of your vehicle. It contains most things you will need to operate and maintain the vehicle, including emergency information.

The DVD includes a computer application containing detailed owner's information which can be viewed on a personal computer or MAC computer. The multimedia DVD also includes videos which can be played on any standard DVD player (including the Uconnect® Touch-Screen Radios). Additional DVD operational information is located on the back of the DVD sleeve.

For complete owner information, refer to your Owner's Manual on the DVD in the owner's kit provided at the time of new vehicle purchase. For your convenience, the information contained on the DVD may also be printed and saved for future reference.

Chrysler Group LLC is committed to protecting our environment and natural resources. By converting from paper to electronic delivery for the majority of the user information for your vehicle, together we greatly reduce the demand for tree-based products and lessen the stress on our environment.

3

INTRODUCTION/WELCOME

VEHICLES SOLD IN CANADA

With respect to any vehicles sold in Canada, the name Chrysler Group LLC shall be deemed to be deleted and the name Chrysler Canada Inc. used in substitution.

WARNING!

- Pedals that cannot move freely can cause loss of vehicle control and increase the risk of serious personal injury.
- Always make sure that objects cannot fall into the driver foot well while the vehicle is moving. Objects can become trapped under the brake pedal and accelerator pedal causing a loss of vehicle control.
- Failure to properly follow floor mat installation or mounting can cause interference with the brake pedal and accelerator pedal operation causing loss of control of the vehicle.
- Never use the 'PARK' position as a substitute for the parking brake. Always apply the parking brake fully when parked to guard against vehicle movement and possible injury or damage.
- Refer to your Owner's Manual on the DVD for further details.

USE OF AFTERMARKET PRODUCTS (ELECTRONICS)

The use of aftermarket devices including cell phones, MP3 players, GPS systems, or chargers may affect the performance of on-board wireless features including Keyless Enter-N-Go™ and Remote Start range. If you are experiencing difficulties with any of your wireless features, try disconnecting your aftermarket devices to see if the situation improves. If your symptoms persist, please see an authorized dealer.

CHRYSLER, DODGE, JEEP, RAM TRUCK, SRT, ATF+4, MOPAR and Uconnect are registered trademarks of Chrysler Group LLC.

COPYRIGHT ©2012 CHRYSLER GROUP LLC

DRIVER COCKPIT

A. Headlight Switch pg. 26

B. Turn Signal/Wiper/Washer/High Beams Lever pg. 25

C. Electronic Vehicle Information Center (EVIC) Controls pg. 101

D. Electronic Vehicle Information Center (EVIC) Display pg. 9

E. Instrument Cluster pg. 8

F. Four Wheel Drive Operation pg. 109

G. Identify Your Audio System pg. 42

H. Audio System Hard Controls pg. 42

I. Power Inverter Outlet pg. 107

J. Manual Climate Controls pg. 33

K. Switch Panel
- Diesel Exhaust Brake
- Tow/Haul pg. 120
- Electronic Stability Control pg. 134
- Air Suspension System
- ParkSense® Rear Park Assist pg. 37
- Tire Pressure Monitoring System for system pg. 38
- Front Heated Seats pg. 22
- Front Ventilated Seats pg. 22
- Heated Steering Wheel pg. 23
- Integrated Trailer Brake Module pg. 120
- Engine Stop Start

L. Shifter

M. Keyless Engine Starting/ Stopping pg. 12

N. Electronic Speed Control pg. 27

O. Hood Release (below steering wheel at base of instrument panel) pg. 160

P. Parking Brake Release

Q. Power Mirrors

R. Power Windows

S. Power Door Locks

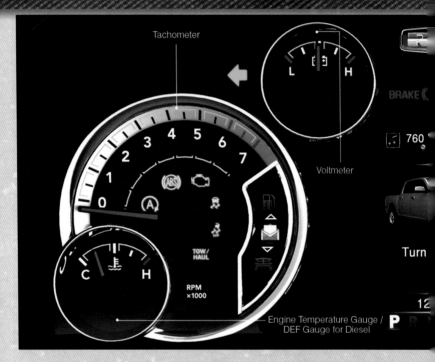

Tachometer

Voltmeter

Engine Temperature Gauge /
DEF Gauge for Diesel

INSTRUMENT CLUSTER

Warning Lights

- Low Fuel Warning Light
- Charging System Light**
- Oil Pressure Warning Light**
- Anti-Lock Brake (ABS) Light**
- Air Bag Warning Light**
- Electronic Throttle Control (ETC) Light
- Engine Temperature Warning Light
- Transmission Temperature Warning Light
- Seat Belt Reminder Light
BRAKE - Brake Warning Light**
- Malfunction Indicator Light (MIL)**
SERV 4WD - SERV (Service) 4WD Indicator Light
- Low Coolant Level Indicator Light

(See page 134 for more information.)

Oil Pressure Gauge

Electronic Vehicle
Information Center

Fuel Gauge

Indicators

⇐⇒ - Turn Signal Indicators

≣D - High Beam Indicator

≣D0≣ - Park/Headlight ON Indicator*

‡O - Front Fog Light Indicator

● - Vehicle Security Indicator*

TOW/ HAUL - TOW/HAUL Indicator

4 LOW - Four-Wheel Drive LOW Mode Indicator

4WD - Four-Wheel Drive and 4LOCK Mode Indicator

4WD AUTO - 4WD Auto Indicator

- Electronic Stability Control (ESC) Indicator Light*

- Electronic Stability Control (ESC) Off Indicator

- Cargo Lamp On Indicator

- Door Ajar Indicator

- Electronic Speed Control Set Indicator

- Check Fuel Filler

TOW/ HAUL - TOW/HAUL Indicator*

 * If equipped

** Bulb Check with Key On

EVIC Messages

NOTE:
Refer to Electronic Vehicle Information Center (EVIC) in this guide or your owners manual for additional information.

GETTING STARTED

KEY FOB

Locking And Unlocking The Doors

- Press and release the UNLOCK button on the RKE transmitter once to unlock the driver's door (EVIC can be setup for driver door first, otherwise this will unlock all doors), or press the unlock button twice within five seconds to unlock all doors, the tailgate and the RamBox® (if equipped). The turn signal lights will flash to acknowledge the unlock signal. The illuminated entry system will also turn on.

- All doors can be programmed to unlock on the first press of the UNLOCK button. Refer to Programmable Features in this guide.

Unlock
Lock
Remote Start
Slide Button to Release Key
Emergency Key

Panic Alarm

- Press the PANIC button once to turn the panic alarm on.

- Wait approximately three seconds and press the button a second time to turn the panic alarm off.

Emergency Key

- Should the battery in the vehicle or the Key Fob transmitter go dead, there is an emergency key located in the Key Fob that can be used for locking and unlocking the doors. To remove the emergency key, slide the button at the top of the Key Fob sideways with your thumb and then pull the key out with your other hand.

WARNING!

- Never leave children alone in a vehicle, or with access to an unlocked vehicle. Allowing children to be in a vehicle unattended is dangerous for a number of reasons. A child or others could be severely injured or killed. Children should be warned not to touch the parking brake, brake pedal, or the shift lever. Do not leave the Key Fob in or near the vehicle, or in a location accessible to children, and do not leave a vehicle equipped with Keyless Enter-N-Go™ in the ACC or ON/RUN mode. A child could start the vehicle, operate power windows, other controls, or move the vehicle.

- Do not leave children or animals inside parked vehicles in hot weather. Interior heat build-up may cause them to be severely injured or killed.

KEYLESS ENTER-N-GO™

- The Keyless Enter-N-Go™ system is an enhancement to the vehicle's Key Fob. This feature allows you to lock and unlock the vehicle's door(s) without having to press the Key Fob lock or unlock buttons, as well as starting and stopping the vehicle with the press of a button.

To Unlock From The Driver or Passenger Side:

- With a valid Keyless Enter-N-Go™ Key Fob located outside the vehicle and within 5 ft (1.5m) of the driver or passenger side door handle, grab either front door handle to unlock the door automatically.

Grab the door handle to unlock

To Lock The Vehicle's Doors

- With a valid Keyless Enter-N-Go™ Key Fob transmitter within 5 ft (1.5 m) of the driver or passenger front door handles, press the door handle LOCK button to lock all doors.

- DO NOT grab the door handle, when pressing the door handle lock button. This could unlock the door(s).

Press the button to lock

Do NOT grab the handle when locking

NOTE:

- After pressing the door handle LOCK button, you must wait two seconds before you can lock or unlock the doors, using either Passive Entry door handle. This is done to allow you to check if the vehicle is locked by pulling the door handle, without the vehicle reacting and unlocking.

- The Passive Entry system will not operate if the RKE transmitter battery is dead.

The vehicle doors can also be locked by using the RKE transmitter lock button or the lock button located on the vehicles interior door panel.

GETTING STARTED

Engine Starting/Stopping

Starting

Engine Start
Stop Button

- With a valid Keyless Enter-N-Go™ Key Fob inside the vehicle.
- Place the shift lever in PARK or NEU-TRAL.
- While pressing the brake pedal, press the ENGINE START/STOP button once. If the engine fails to start, the starter will disengage automatically after 10 seconds.
- To stop the cranking of the engine prior to the engine starting, press the button again.

NOTE:

In case the ignition switch does not change with the push of a button, the RKE transmitter (Key Fob) may have a low or dead battery. In this situation a back up method can be used to operate the ignition switch. Put the nose side of the Key Fob against the ENGINE START/STOP button and push to operate the ignition switch.

Stopping

- Place the shift lever in PARK.
- Press the ENGINE START/STOP button once. The ignition switch will return to the OFF position.
- **If the shift lever is not in PARK, the ENGINE START/STOP button must be held for two seconds and vehicle speed must be above 5 mph (8 km/h) before the engine will shut off.**

REMOTE START

- Press the REMOTE START button ⟳² on the Key Fob twice within five seconds. Pressing the REMOTE START ⟳² button a third time shuts the engine off.
- To drive the vehicle, press the UNLOCK button, insert the Key Fob in the ignition and turn to the ON/RUN position.
- With remote start, the engine will only run for 15 minutes (timeout) unless the ignition Key Fob is placed in the ON/RUN position.
- The vehicle must be started with the Key Fob after two consecutive timeouts.

WARNING!
• Do not start or run an engine in a closed garage or confined area. Exhaust gas contains Carbon Monoxide (CO) which is odorless and colorless. Carbon Monoxide is poisonous and can cause you or others to be severely injured or killed when inhaled. • Keep Key Fob transmitters away from children. Operation of the Remote Start System, windows, door locks or other controls could cause you and others to be severely injured or killed.

THEFT ALARM

To Arm:

• Press the Key Fob LOCK button or the power door lock switch while the door is open.

To Disarm:

• Press the Key Fob UNLOCK button or turn the ignition to the ON/RUN position.

SEAT BELT

• Be sure everyone in your vehicle is in a seat and using a seat belt properly.

• Position the lap belt across your thighs, below your abdomen. To remove slack in the lap portion, pull up a bit on the shoulder belt. To loosen the lap belt if it is too tight, tilt the latch plate and pull on the lap belt. A snug belt reduces the risk of sliding under the belt in a collision.

• Position the shoulder belt on your chest so that it is comfortable and not resting on your neck. The retractor will withdraw any slack in the belt.

• A shoulder belt placed behind you will not protect you from injury during a collision. You are more likely to hit your head in a collision if you do not wear your shoulder belt. The lap and shoulder belt are meant to be used together.

• A belt that is too loose will not protect you properly. In a sudden stop you could move too far forward, increasing the possibility of injury. Wear your seat belt snugly.

• A frayed or torn belt could rip apart in a collision and leave you with no protection. Inspect the belt system periodically, checking for cuts, frays, or loose parts. Damaged parts must be replaced immediately. Do not disassemble or modify the system. Seat belt assemblies must be replaced after a collision if they have been damaged (bent retractor, torn webbing, etc.).

• The seat belts for both front seating positions are equipped with pretensioning devices that are designed to remove slack from the seat belt in the event of a collision.

• A deployed pretensioner or a deployed air bag must be replaced immediately.

GETTING STARTED

SUPPLEMENTAL RESTRAINT SYSTEM (SRS) — AIR BAGS

- This vehicle has Advanced Front Air Bags for both the driver and right front passenger as a supplement to the seat belt restraint system. The Advanced Front Air Bags will not deploy in every type of collision.

- Advanced Front Air Bags are designed to provide additional protection by supplementing the seat belts in certain frontal collisions depending on several factors, including the severity and type of collision. Advanced Front Air Bags are not expected to reduce the risk of injury in rear, side, or rollover collisions.

- This vehicle is equipped with Supplemental Side Air Bag Inflatable Curtains to protect the driver, front and rear passengers sitting next to a window.

- This vehicle is equipped with Supplemental Seat-Mounted Side Air Bags to provide enhanced protection to help protect an occupant during a side impact.

- If the Air Bag Warning Light 🚶 is not on during starting, stays on, or turns on while driving, have the vehicle serviced by an authorized service center immediately.

- Refer to the Owner's Manual on the DVD for further details regarding the Supplemental Restraint System (SRS).

WARNING!

- Relying on the air bags alone could lead to more severe injuries in a collision. The air bags work with your seat belt to restrain you properly. In some collisions, the air bags won't deploy at all. Always wear your seat belts even though you have air bags.
- Being too close to the steering wheel or instrument panel during Advanced Front Air Bag deployment could cause serious injury, including death. Air bags need room to inflate. Sit back, comfortably extending your arms to reach the steering wheel or instrument panel.
- Supplemental Side Air Bag Inflatable Curtains and Supplemental Seat-Mounted Side Air Bags need room to inflate. Do not lean against the door or window. Sit upright in the center of the seat.
- Being too close to the Supplemental Side Air Bag Inflatable Curtain and/or Seat-Mounted Side Air Bag during deployment could cause you to be severely injured or killed.
- Do not drive your vehicle after the air bags have deployed. If you are involved in another collision, the air bags will not be in place to protect you.
- After any collision, the vehicle should be taken to an authorized dealer immediately.

CHILD RESTRAINTS

- Children 12 years and under should ride properly buckled up in a rear seat, if available. According to crash statistics, children are safer when properly restrained in the rear seats rather than in the front.

- Every state in the United States and all Canadian provinces require that small children ride in proper restraint systems. This is the law, and you can be prosecuted for ignoring it.

NOTE:
For additional information, refer to www.seatcheck.org or call 1–866–SEATCHECK. Canadian residents, should refer to Transport Canada's website for additional information.
http://www.tc.gc.ca/eng/roadsafety/safedrivers-childsafety-index-53.htm

Installing The LATCH - Compatible Child Restraint System

- Your vehicle's second row passenger seats are equipped with the child restraint anchorage system called LATCH, which stands for Lower Anchors and Tether for CHildren. LATCH child restraint anchorage systems are installed in the rear seat outboard positions.

- LATCH equipped seating positions have both lower anchor bars, located at the back of the seat cushion, and tether strap anchorages, located behind the seat back.

GETTING STARTED

Installing The Lower Attachments:

- The vehicle lower anchorages are round bars located at the rear of the seat cushion where it meets the seatback. The rear seat lower anchors can be readily identified by the symbol ![icon] located on the seatback directly above the anchorages and are just visible when you lean into the rear seat to install the child restraint.

- Loosen the child seat adjusters on the lower straps and on the tether strap so that you can attach the hooks or connectors to the vehicle anchors more easily.

Lower Anchors ─

- Attach the lower hooks or connectors over the top of the seatcover material.

- Then tighten the straps as you push the child restraint rearward and downward into the seat.

Tether Anchorage Points At The Right And Center Front Seat (Regular Cab - All Seats):

- Place the child restraint on the seat and adjust the tether strap so that it will reach over the seat back under the head restraint to the tether anchor directly behind the seat.

- Lift the cover (if equipped), and attach the hook to the square opening in the sheet metal.

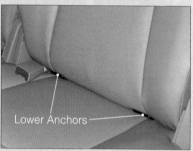

Tether Anchors
(fold cover
downward)

- Install the child restraint and remove the slack in the tether strap according to the manufacturer's instructions.

Child Restraint Installation Sequence (Mega Cab® - Rear Seats):

- Place a child restraint on each outboard rear seat and adjust the tether strap so that it will reach under the head restraint to the tether anchor directly behind the seat.

- Lift the cover, and attach the hook to the square opening in the sheet metal.

- Install the child restraint and remove the slack in the tether strap according to the manufacturer's instructions.

Child Restraints Installation Sequence (Quad Cab®/Crew Cab - Rear Seats)

The top tether anchorages in this vehicle are tether strap loops located between the rear glass and the back of the rear seat. There is a tether strap loop located behind each seating position. Follow the steps below to attach the tether strap of the child restraint.

Right or Left Outboard Seats:

1. Raise the head restraint and reach between the rear seat and rear glass to access the tether strap loop.

| Head Restraint In Raised Position | Tether Strap Loop With Center Head Restraint In Raised Position |

2. Place a child restraint on the seat and adjust the tether strap so that it will reach over the seat back, under the head restraint, through the tether strap loop behind the seat and over to the tether strap loop behind the center seat.

3. Pass the tether strap hook under the head restraint behind the child seat, through the tether strap loop behind the seat and over to the center tether strap loop.

Tether Strap Through Outboard Tether Strap Loop

4. Attach the hook to the center tether strap loop (see diagram). Tighten the tether strap according to the child seat manufacturer's instructions.

Tether Strap Through Outboard Tether Strap Loop And Attached To Center Tether Strap Loop

GETTING STARTED

NOTE:
If there are child seats in both of the outboard (left and right) seating positions, the tether strap hooks of both child seats should be connected to the center tether strap loop. This is the correct way to tether two outboard child seats.

Center Seat:

1. Raise the head restraint and reach between the rear seat and rear glass to access the tether strap loop.

2. Place a child restraint on the seat and adjust the tether strap so that it will reach over the seat back, under the head restraint, through the tether strap loop behind the seat and over to the tether strap loop behind either the right or left outboard seat.

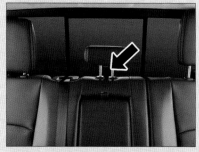

3. Pass the tether strap hook under the head restraint behind the child seat, through the tether strap loop behind the seat and over to the right or left outboard tether strap loop.

Tether Strap Loop With Head Restraint In Raised Position

4. Attach the hook to the outboard tether strap loop (see diagram). Tighten the tether strap according to the child seat manufacturer's instructions.

Tether Strap Through Center Tether Strap Loop

Tether Strap Through Center Tether Strap Loop And Attached To Outboard Tether Strap Loop

Installing Three Child Restraints:

1. Place a child restraint on each outboard rear seat. Route the tether straps following the directions for right and left seating positions, above.

2. Attach both hooks to the center tether strap loop, but do not tighten the straps yet.

3. Place a child restraint on the center rear seat. Route the tether strap following the directions for the center seating position, above.

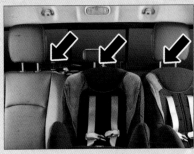

Left Outboard And Center Seating Position Shown

4. Attach the hook to the outboard tether strap loop.

5. Tighten the tether straps according to the child seat manufacturer's instructions, tightening the right and left tether straps before the center tether strap.

Installing The Child Restraint Using The Vehicle Seat Belts

• To install a child restraint, first, pull enough of the seat belt webbing from the retractor to route it through the belt path of the child restraint and slide the latch plate into the buckle.

• Next, extract all the seat belt webbing out of the retractor and then allow the belt to retract into the retractor. Finally, pull on any excess webbing to tighten the lap portion around the child restraint. Any seat belt system will loosen with time, so check the belt occasionally, and pull it tight if necessary.

• Route the tether strap to provide the most direct path for the strap between the anchor and the child seat, preferably between the head restraint posts underneath the head restraint.

• Attach the tether strap hook of the child restraint to the tether anchor and remove slack in the tether strap according to the child restraint manufacturer's instructions.

NOTE:
Ensure that the tether strap does not slip into the opening between the seatbacks as you remove slack in the strap.

GETTING STARTED

FRONT SEATS

Power Seats

- The seat switch controls forward/backward and up/down.
- The recline switch controls the angle of the seatback. Push switch forward or rearward and the seatback will move in either direction.

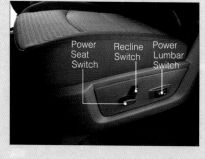

Power Seat Switch   Recline Switch   Power Lumbar Switch

Power Lumbar

- The lumbar controls are located on the outboard side of the seat cushion. The lumbar support can be increased by pressing the front of the switch and decreased by pressing the back of the switch.

Memory Seat

Driver's Memory Buttons

- The memory seat feature allows you to save the driver's seat position (excluding lumbar position), driver's outside mirror position, adjustable brake and accelerator pedals, Automatic Temperature Control (ATC) temperature setting and radio station preset settings. The driver's memory buttons are located on the outboard side of the driver's seat cushion.

- Adjust all memory profile settings, press the middle button S (SET), then press 1 or 2 within five seconds.

- To program a Key Fob to the memory position, place the ignition switch in the LOCK position and remove the Key Fob, press and release the LOCK button on the Key Fob to be programmed within 5 seconds of pressing button 1 or 2.

- Press 1 or 2 to recall the saved positions, or press UNLOCK on the programmed Key Fob.

- Refer to the Owner's Manual on the DVD for further details.

Manual Seats

Forward/Rearward

Recliner Lever   Adjusting Bar

- Lift up on the adjusting bar located at the front of the seat near the floor and release at the desired position. Then, using body pressure, move forward and backward on the seat to be sure that the seat adjusters have latched.

Recliner

- Lift the recliner lever located on the outboard side of the seat, lean back and release at the desired position.

CAUTION!

Do not place any article under a power seat or impede its ability to move as it may cause damage to the seat controls. Seat travel may become limited if movement is stopped by an obstruction in the seat's path.

GETTING STARTED

WARNING!

- Adjusting a seat while the vehicle is moving is dangerous. The sudden movement of the seat could cause you to lose control. The seat belt might not be properly adjusted, and you could be severely injured or killed. Only adjust a seat while the vehicle is parked.
- Actuating the recliner handle will allow the seatback to swing (dump) forward on manual recliner seats. Do not stand or lean in front of the seat while actuating the handle. The seatback may swing forward and hit you, causing injury. This dump feature allows access to the storage bin behind the seat. To avoid injury, place your hand on the seatback and actuate the handle, then position the seatback in the desired position.
- Do not ride with the seatback reclined so that the seat belt is no longer resting against your chest. In a collision, you could slide under the seat belt and be severely injured or killed. Use the recliner only when the vehicle is parked.

HEATED/VENTILATED SEATS

Front Heated Seats

- The controls for front heated seats are located on the center instrument panel below the climate controls and there are soft keys in the radio that control the front heated seats.

- Press the switch once to select High-level heating. Press the switch a second time to select Low-level heating. Press the switch a third time to shut the heating elements Off.

- If the High-level setting is selected, the system will automatically switch to Low-level after approximately 20 minutes. The Low-level setting will turn Off automatically after approximately 40 minutes.

Ventilated
Seat Switches

Heated Seat Switches

Front Ventilated Seats

- Located in the seat cushion are small fans that draw the air from the passenger compartment and pull air through fine perforations in the seat cover to help keep the driver and front passenger cooler in higher ambient temperatures.

- The ventilated seat switches are located in the switch bank in the center stack of the instrument panel just below the climate controls as well as soft keys in the radio. The fans operate at two speeds, HIGH and LOW. Press the switch once to select High speed. Press the switch a second time to select Low speed. Press the switch a third time to turn the fans Off.

REAR HEATED SEATS

- Second row heated seat switches are located on the rear of the center console.

- Press the switch once to select High-level heating. Press the switch a second time to select Low-level heating. Press the switch a third time to shut the heating elements Off.

- If the High-level setting is selected, the system will automatically switch to Low-level after approximately 20 minutes. The Low-level setting will turn Off automatically after approximately 40 minutes.

Rear Heated Seat Switches

WARNING!

- Persons who are unable to feel pain to the skin because of advanced age, chronic illness, diabetes, spinal cord injury, medication, alcohol use, exhaustion or other physical conditions must exercise care when using the seat heater. It may cause burns even at low temperatures, especially if used for long periods of time.

- Do not place anything on the seat that insulates against heat, such as a blanket or cushion. This may cause the seat heater to overheat. Sitting in a seat that has been overheated could cause serious burns due to the increased surface temperature of the seat.

HEATED STEERING WHEEL

- The steering wheel contains a heating element that heats the steering wheel to one temperature setting.

- The heated steering wheel switch is located on the center instrument panel below the climate controls.

- The heated steering wheel is also controlled by soft keys in the radio screen.

- Press the switch once to turn the heating element On. Press the switch a second time to turn the heating element Off.

Heated Steering
Wheel Switch

- Once the heated steering wheel has been turned on, it will operate for approximately 30 to 95 minutes before automatically shutting off. The heated steering wheel can shut off early or may not turn on when the steering wheel is already warm.

TILT STEERING COLUMN

- The tilt lever is located on the steering column below the turn signal lever.
- To tilt the column, simply pull the tilt lever rearward toward you and then move the steering wheel upward or downward as desired.
- Release the tilt lever to lock the steering wheel into position.

ADJUSTABLE PEDALS

- Press the switch located on the left side of the steering column forward to move the brake and accelerator pedals away from the driver and press the switch rearward to move the pedals closer to the driver.

Adjustable Pedal Switch

Tilt Lever

NOTE:

The pedals cannot be adjusted when the vehicle is in REVERSE or when the Electronic Speed Control is set.

CAUTION!
Do not place any article under the adjustable pedals or impede its ability to move, as it may cause damage to the pedal controls. Pedal travel may become limited if movement is stopped by an obstruction in the adjustable pedal's path.

WARNING!
• Tilting the steering column while the vehicle is moving is dangerous. Without a stable steering column, you could lose control of the vehicle and have a collision. Adjust the column only while the vehicle is stopped. Be sure it is locked before driving. • Do not adjust the pedals while the vehicle is moving. You could lose control and have a collision. Always adjust the pedals while the vehicle is parked.

ENGINE BREAK-IN RECOMMENDATIONS

- A long break-in period is not required for the engine and drivetrain (transmission and axle) in your vehicle.

- Drive moderately during the first 300 miles (500 km). After the initial 60 miles (100 km), speeds up to 50 or 55 mph (80 or 90 km/h) are desirable.

- While cruising, brief full-throttle acceleration within the limits of local traffic laws contributes to a good break-in. Wide-open throttle acceleration in low gear can be detrimental and should be avoided.

- The engine oil installed in the engine at the factory is a high-quality energy conserving type lubricant. Oil changes should be consistent with anticipated climate conditions under which vehicle operations will occur. For the recommended viscosity and quality grades, refer to "Maintaining Your Vehicle".

NOTE:
A new engine may consume some oil during its first few thousand miles (kilometers) of operation. This should be considered a normal part of the break-in and not interpreted as an indication of difficulty.

CAUTION!

Never use Non-Detergent Oil or Straight Mineral Oil in the engine or damage may result.

DIESEL ENGINE BREAK-IN RECOMMENDATIONS

For diesel engine break-in recommendations, refer to Diesel Engine Break-In Recommendations on pg. 124

TURN SIGNALS/WIPER/WASHER/HIGH BEAMS LEVER

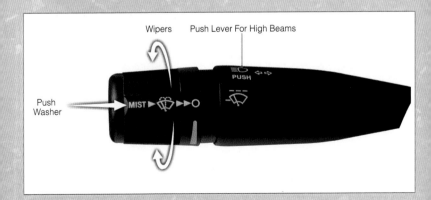

OPERATING YOUR VEHICLE

Turn Signals/Lane Change Assist

- Tap the lever up or down once and the turn signal (right or left) will flash three times and automatically turn off.

Wipers

Intermittent, Low And High Operation

- Rotate the end of the lever to the first detent position for one of five intermittent settings, the second detent for low wiper operation and the third detent for high wiper operation.

Washer Operation

- Push the end of the lever inward to the second detent and hold for as long as spray is desired.

Mist Feature

- When a single wipe to clear off road mist or spray from a passing vehicle is needed, push the washer knob, located on the end of the multifunction lever, inward to the first detent and release. The wipers will cycle one time and automatically shut off.

High Beams

- Push the lever away from you to activate the high beams.
- A high beam symbol will illuminate in the cluster to indicate the high beams are on.

NOTE:

For safe driving, turn off the high beams when oncoming traffic is present to prevent headlight glare and as a courtesy to other motorists.

HEADLIGHT SWITCH

Automatic Headlights/Parking Lights/Headlights

- Rotate the headlight switch, located on the instrument panel to the left of the steering wheel, to the first detent ⫶D0⫶ for parking lights and to the second detent for headlights ⫶D.

- With the parking lights or low beam headlights on, push the headlight switch once for fog lights.
- Rotate the headlight switch to "AUTO" for AUTO headlights.
- When set to AUTO, the system automatically turns the headlights on or off based on ambient light levels.

SmartBeams™

- This system automatically controls the use of the headlight high beams. Refer to Programmable Features in Electronics for further details.

Instrument Panel Dimmer

- Rotate the dimmer control to the extreme left position to fully dim the instrument panel lights and prevent the interior lights from illuminating when a door is opened.
- Rotate the dimmer control right to increase the brightness of the instrument panel when the parking lights or headlights are on.
- Rotate the dimmer control right to the next detent position to fully brighten the odometer and radio when the parking lights or headlights are on. Refer to your Media Center/Radio User Manual on the DVD for display dimming.
- Rotate the dimmer control right to the last detent position to turn on the interior lighting.

Cargo Light

- The cargo light is strategically placed lighting that helps illuminate the bed area of the truck. A cargo light symbol will illuminate in the cluster to indicate the light is on.
- Push the button to turn ON/OFF the cargo lighting.

SPEED CONTROL

- The speed control switches are located on the steering wheel.

OPERATING YOUR VEHICLE

Cruise ON/OFF

- Push the ON/OFF switch to activate the Speed Control.
- The cruise symbol ⟨🕑⟩ will appear on the instrument cluster to indicate the Speed Control is on.
- Push the ON/OFF switch a second time to turn the system off.

Set ⟨🕑⟩

- With the Speed Control on, push and release the SET/DECEL switch to set a desired speed.

Accel/Decel

- Push and hold the RESUME/ACCEL switch to accelerate or push and hold the SET/DECEL switch to decelerate the vehicle; release the switch to save the new set speed.
- Once a speed is set, pushing the RESUME/ACCEL switch once or the SET/DECEL switch once will increase or decrease the set speed approximately 1 mph (2 km/h).

Resume

- To resume a previously selected set speed in memory, push the RESUME/ACCEL switch and release.

Cancel

- Push the CANCEL switch or apply the brakes to cancel the set speed and maintain the set speed memory.
- Push the ON/OFF switch to turn the system off and erase the set speed memory.

WARNING!

- Leaving the Electronic Speed Control system on when not in use is dangerous. You could accidentally set the system or cause it to go faster than you want. You could lose control and have a collision. Always leave the Electronic Speed Control system off when you are not using it.
- Electronic Speed Control can be dangerous where the system cannot maintain a constant speed. Your vehicle could go too fast for the conditions, and you could lose control. A collision could be the result. Do not use Electronic Speed Control in heavy traffic or on roads that are winding, icy, snow-covered or slippery.

EIGHT–SPEED AUTOMATIC TRANSMISSION — IF EQUIPPED

- Your vehicle is equipped with a state of the art, fuel efficient eight-speed transmission. The electronic Transmission Shifter is located on the instrument panel. The transmission gear (PRND) is displayed both above the shifter control and in the Electronic Vehicle Information Center (EVIC).

- To select a gear range, simply rotate the shifter control.

NOTE:
You must press the brake pedal to shift the transmission out of PARK or from NEUTRAL into DRIVE or REVERSE.

Rotate Gear Selector Knob

- To shift past multiple gear ranges at once (such as Park to Drive), simply rotate the switch to the appropriate detent.

- Select the DRIVE range for normal driving.

ELECTRONIC RANGE SELECT (ERS) OPERATION

Move Console Shifter Left (-) or Right (+)

Toggle the Switch Down (-) or Up (+)

- Electronic Range Select (ERS) allows you to limit the highest available transmission gear, and can be activated during any driving condition. When towing a trailer or operating the vehicle in off-road conditions, using ERS shift control will help you maximize both performance and engine braking.

- Move the console shift lever left (-) or right (+), or toggle the switch on the column shift lever down (-) or up (+) to select the desired top gear.

- For maximum deceleration (engine braking) move the console shift lever left (-) and hold, or toggle the switch on the column shift lever down (-) and hold. Your vehicle will automatically select the lowest safe gear for optimal engine braking.

- To disable ERS, push and hold the console shift lever to the right (+) or push and hold the column shift lever switch up (+) until "D" is displayed in the odometer.

- Switching between ERS and DRIVE mode can be done at any vehicle speed.

- Refer to your Owner's Manual on the DVD for further details.

OPERATING YOUR VEHICLE

ELECTRONIC RANGE SELECT (ERS) OPERATION – 8 SPEED TRANSMISSION

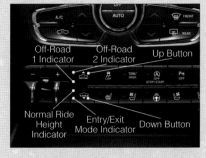

- The Electronic Range Select (ERS) shift control allows the driver to limit the highest available gear when the transmission shifter switch is in the DRIVE position

- You can switch between DRIVE and ERS mode at any vehicle speed.

- Tapping the ERS (-) switch (on the steering wheel) will activate ERS mode.

- Once in ERS mode, tapping the ERS (-) or (+) switch will change the top available gear.

- To exit ERS mode, simply press and hold the ERS (+) switch until "D" is once again displayed in the transmission gear position indicator in the instrument cluster.

AIR SUSPENSION SYSTEM

- The air suspension system provides full time load leveling capability along with the benefit of being able to adjust vehicle height by the push of a button.

- Automatic height changes will occur based on vehicle speed and the current vehicle height. The indicator lamps and EVIC messages will operate the same for automatic changes and user requested changes.

Description

- **Normal Ride Height (NRH)** - This is the standard position of the suspension and is meant for normal driving.

- **Off-Road 1 (OR1) (Raises the vehicle approximately 1 in (26 mm)** This position should be the primary position for all off-road driving until Off Road 2 (OR2) is needed. A smoother and more comfortable ride will result. To enter OR1, press the "Up" button once from the NRH position while the vehicle speed is below 35 mph (56 km/h). When in the OR1 position, if the vehicle speed remains between 40 mph (64 km/h) and 50 mph (80 km/h) for greater than 20 seconds or if the vehicle speed exceeds 50 mph (80 km/h), the vehicle will be automatically lowered to NRH. Off-Road 1 may not be available due to vehicle payload, an EVIC message will be displayed when this occurs. Refer to "Electronic Vehicle Information Center (EVIC)" in "Understanding Your Instrument Panel" for further information.

- **Off-Road 2 (OR2) (Raises the vehicle approximately 2 in (51 mm)** - This position is intended for off-roading use only where maximum ground clearance is required. To enter OR2, press the "Up" button twice from the NRH position or once from the OR1 position while vehicle speed is below 20 mph (32 km/h). While in OR2, if the vehicle speed exceeds 25 mph (40 km/h) the vehicle height will be automatically lowered to OR1. Off-Road 2 may not be available due to vehicle payload, an EVIC message will be displayed when this occurs. Refer to "Electronic Vehicle Information Center (EVIC)" in "Understanding Your Instrument Panel" for further information.

- **Aero Mode (Lowers the vehicle approximately .6 in (15 mm) – 1500 Models Only** - This position provides improved aerodynamics by lowering the vehicle. The vehicle will automatically enter Aero Mode when the vehicle speed remains between 62 mph (100 km/h) and 66 mph (106 km/h) for greater than 20 seconds or if the vehicle speed exceeds 66 mph (106 km/h). The vehicle will return to NRH from Aero Mode if the vehicle speed remains between 30 mph (48 km/h) and 35 mph (56 km/h) for greater than 20 seconds or if the vehicle speed falls below 30 mph (48 km/h).

NOTE:

Aero Mode may be disabled through vehicle settings in the Electronic Vehicle Information Center (EVIC) or in the Uconnect™ Access 8.4 Radio (If Equipped).

- **Entry/Exit Mode (Lowers the vehicle approximately 2 in (51 mm)** - This position lowers the vehicle for easier passenger entry and exit as well as lowering the rear of the vehicle for easier loading and unloading of cargo. To enter Entry/Exit Mode, press the "Down" button once from the NHR while the vehicle speed is below 33 mph (53 km/h). Once the vehicle speed goes below 15 mph (24 km/h) the vehicle height will begin to lower. If the vehicle speed remains between 15 mph (24 km/h) and 25 mph (40 km/h) for greater than 60 seconds, or the vehicle speed exceeds 25 mph (40 km/h) the Entry/Exit change will be cancelled. To return to Normal Height Mode, press the "Up" button once while in Entry/Exit or drive the vehicle over 15 mph (24 km/h). Entry/Exit mode may not be available due to vehicle payload, an EVIC message will be displayed when this occurs. Refer to "Electronic Vehicle Information Center (EVIC)" in "Understanding Your Instrument Panel" for further information.

- Refer to your Owner's Manual on the DVD for further details.

Air Suspension Modes

- The Air Suspension system has multiple modes to protect the system in unique situations:

Tire Jack Mode

- To assist with changing a spare tire, the air suspension system has a feature which allows the automatic leveling to be disabled. Refer to "Electronic Vehicle Information Center (EVIC)" in "Understanding Your Instrument Panel" for further information.

Transport Mode

- To assist with flat bed towing, the air suspension system has a feature which will put the vehicle into Entry/Exit height and disable the automatic load leveling system. Refer to "Electronic Vehicle Information Center (EVIC)" in "Understanding Your Instrument Panel" for further information.

Wheel Alignment Mode

- Before performing a wheel alignment this mode must be enabled. Refer to "Electronic Vehicle Information Center (EVIC)" in "Understanding Your Instrument Panel" for further information.

Protection Mode

- In order to "protect" the air suspension system, the vehicle will enter Protection Mode when the payload has been exceeded or load leveling cannot be achieved. Refer to "Electronic Vehicle Information Center (EVIC)" in "Understanding Your Instrument Panel" for further information.

MANUAL CLIMATE CONTROLS WITHOUT TOUCH-SCREEN

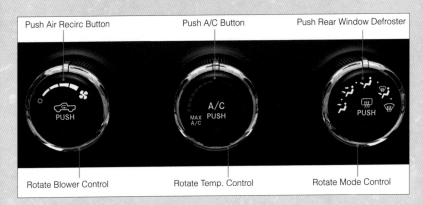

Push Air Recirc Button — Push A/C Button — Push Rear Window Defroster

Rotate Blower Control — Rotate Temp. Control — Rotate Mode Control

Air Recirculation /Max A/C

- Rotate the Temperature Control to the MAX A/C position to automatically turn on both Air Conditioning and Recirculation.

OPERATING YOUR VEHICLE

- For window defogging, turn the recirculation button off.
- Recirculation is not allowed in defrost
- Recirculation is allowed in floor mode and defrost/floor (mix modes) for approximately five minutes.

Heated Mirrors

- The mirrors are heated to melt frost or ice. This feature is activated whenever you turn on the defroster.

MANUAL CLIMATE CONTROLS WITH TOUCH-SCREEN

Touch-Screen Manual Climate Controls

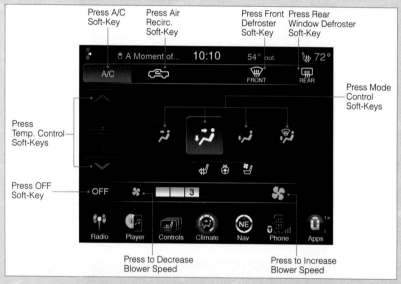

Climate Control Knobs

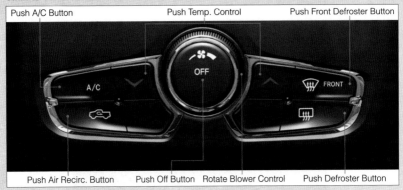

Push A/C Button   Push Temp. Control   Push Front Defroster Button

Push Air Recirc. Button   Push Off Button   Rotate Blower Control   Push Defroster Button

Air Recirculation

- Use recirculation for maximum A/C operation.
- For window defogging, turn the recirculation button off.

Heated Mirrors

- The mirrors are heated to melt frost or ice. This feature is activated whenever you turn on the defroster.

OPERATING YOUR VEHICLE

AUTOMATIC CLIMATE CONTROLS WITH TOUCH-SCREEN

Touch-Screen Automatic Climate Controls

Press A/C Soft-Key

Press Air Recirc. Soft-Key

Press AUTO Soft-Key

Press Front Defroster Soft-Key

Press Rear Window Defroster Soft-Key

Press Mode Control Soft-Key

Passenger Temp. Controls

Press SYNC Soft-Key

Driver Temp. Controls

Press OFF Soft-Key

Press To Decrease Blower Speed

Press To Increase Blower Speed

Climate Control Knobs

Push Off Button

Rotate Blower Control

Push A/C Button

Push Front Defroster Button

Push Air Recirc. Button

Push Driver Temp. Controls

Push AUTO

Push Passenger Temp. Controls

Push Defroster Button

- Press the AUTO button or AUTO soft-key.
- Select the desired temperature by pushing the up or down temperature buttons for the driver or passenger.
- The system will maintain the set temperature automatically.

Air Conditioning (A/C)

- If the air conditioning button is pressed while in AUTO mode, the system will exit AUTO mode and stay in A/C. The mode and blower will be set at the closest mode and blower position that the system was operating in AUTO.

SYNC Temperature Soft-Key

- Touch the SYNC soft-key on the Uconnect® Access radio to control the driver and passenger temperatures simultaneously. Touch the SYNC soft-key a second time to control the temperatures individually.

Air Recirculation ⌒⊆⊃

- Use recirculation for maximum A/C operation.
- For window defogging, turn the recirculation button off.
- If the Recirculation button is pushed while in the AUTO mode, the indicator light may flash three times to indicate the cabin air is being controlled automatically.

Heated Mirrors

- The mirrors are heated to melt frost or ice. This feature is activated whenever you turn on the defroster.

PARKSENSE® REAR PARK ASSIST

- If an object is detected behind the rear bumper while the vehicle is in REVERSE, a warning will display in the instrument cluster and a tone, that changes speed depending on the distance of the object from the bumper, will sound.

Service The ParkSense® Rear Park Assist System

- When the ParkSense® Rear Park Assist System is malfunctioning, the instrument cluster will actuate a single chime, once per ignition cycle, and it will display the "CLEAN PARK ASSIST SENSORS" or the "SERVICE PARK ASSIST SYSTEM" message.
- If "CLEAN PARK ASSIST SENSORS" appears in the Electronic Vehicle Information Center (EVIC) and the rear fascia/bumper is clean and clear of snow, ice, mud, dirt or other obstruction, see your authorized dealer.
- If "SERVICE PARK ASSIST SYSTEM" appears in the EVIC, see your authorized dealer.

Enable/Disable ParkSense®

- ParkSense® can be enabled and disabled with a switch located in the switch bank of the instrument panel or through the Customer-Programmable Features section of the EVIC. When the switch is pressed to disable the system, the instrument cluster will display the "PARK ASSIST SYSTEM OFF" message for approximately five seconds.

OPERATING YOUR VEHICLE

PARKVIEW® REAR BACK-UP CAMERA

- You can see an on-screen image of the rear surroundings of your vehicle whenever the shift lever is put into REVERSE. The ParkView® Rear Back-Up Camera image will be displayed in the rearview mirror or touchscreen display along with a caution note to "check entire surroundings" across the top of the screen. After five seconds this note will disappear.

- If the rearview mirror or touchscreen display appears foggy, clean the ParkView® camera located to the left of the tailgate handle.

WARNING!

Drivers must be careful when backing up; even when using the ParkView® Rear Back-Up Camera. Always check carefully behind your vehicle, and be sure to check for pedestrians, animals, other vehicles, obstructions, or blind spots before backing up. You must continue to pay attention while backing up. Failure to do so can result in serious injury or death.

TIRE PRESSURE MONITOR SYSTEM (TPMS) – 2500 MODELS ONLY

Tire Light Load Inflation Switch Description

- The Tire Pressure Monitoring System on your vehicle has two different tire pressure settings based on vehicle loading. The Tire Light Load Switch is located on the Instrument Panel below the climate controls.

- The "Light Load Inflation" and "Max Load Inflation" tire pressures recommended for your vehicle based on vehicle loading are found on the Supplemental Tire Pressure Information Label located on the rear face of the driver front door.

- When the vehicle is in the "Light Load Inflation" setting, the Tire Light Load Inflation switch is On. The indicator light is Off when in the "Max Load Inflation" setting.

Light Load Inflation (Indicator Light On)

- If the passenger and cargo weights are less than the Light Load Pressure Definition shown on the Supplemental Tire Pressure Information Label, inflate or deflate tires to the correct "Light Load Inflation" pressure. If the indicator light is not on, **the mode can be changed by pushing the switch once.**

- If the light on the switch flashes On and Off, **after the button is pressed to switch between modes, this indicates conditions are not correct to switch modes.** The system will not allow switching modes until the tire pressures have been set to Light Load Inflation as indicated on the Supplemental Tire Pressure Information Label.

- IF THE LIGHT STARTS FLASHING TO SHOW LOW AIR PRESSURE, BRING THE AIR PRESSURE IN THAT TIRE TO THE PLACARD VALUE SHOWN ON THE LABEL ON THE DRIVER DOOR. NOTE: AFTER INFLATION, THE VEHICLE MAY NEED TO BE DRIVEN FOR UP TO 20 MINUTES BEFORE THE FLASHING LIGHT WILL GO OFF.

Max Load Inflation (Indicator Light Off)

- If the passenger and cargo weights exceed the Light Load Pressure Definition shown on the Supplemental Tire Pressure Information Label, adjust tires to the correct "Max Load Inflation" pressure. If the indicator is on, reset by pushing the switch once.

- If the tire pressure monitoring light and a "low tire" message appears in the cluster, inflate the tire pressures to the "Max Load Inflation" setting as indicated in the Supplemental Tire Pressure Information Label.

- **After any tire pressure adjustment, the vehicle may need to be driven for up to 20 minutes at speeds over 15 mph for the tire pressure information to be updated, or for a low tire pressure warning to go out.**

- For additional information, refer to the Owner's Manual on the DVD.

POWER SLIDING REAR WINDOW

- The switch for the power sliding rear window is located on the overhead console.
- Push the switch right to open the glass and pull the switch left to close the glass.

Power Sliding
Rear Window Switch

OPERATING YOUR VEHICLE

POWER SUNROOF

- The power sunroof switch is located on the overhead console.

Opening Sunroof

Express

- Press the switch rearward and release. The sunroof will fully open and stop automatically.

Power Sunroof Switch

Closing Sunroof

Express

- Press the switch forward and release. The sunroof will close automatically from any position.

Manual Open/Close

- Press and hold the switch rearward to open or forward to close the sunroof. Any release of the switch will stop the movement, and the sunroof will remain in a partially open or closed position until the switch is pressed again.

Venting Sunroof

- Press and release the "VENT" button, and the sunroof will open to the vent position. This is called "Express Vent" and will occur regardless of sunroof position. During Express Vent operation, any movement of the switch will stop the sunroof.

Pinch Protection Feature

- This feature will detect an obstruction in the opening of the sunroof during Express Close operation. If an obstruction in the path of the sunroof is detected, the sunroof will automatically retract. Remove the obstruction if this occurs. Next, press the switch forward and release to Express Close.

NOTE:

If three consecutive sunroof close attempts result in Pinch Protect reversals, the fourth close attempt will be a Manual Close movement with Pinch Protect disabled.

WARNING!

- Never leave children in a vehicle, and do not leave the key in the ignition switch (or leave the ignition of a vehicle equipped with Keyless Enter-N-Go™ in the ACC or ON/Run position). Occupants, particularly unattended children, can become entrapped by the power sunroof while operating the power sunroof switch. Such entrapment may result in serious injury or death.
- In a collision, there is a greater risk of being thrown from a vehicle with an open sunroof. You could also be severely injured or killed. Always fasten your seat belt properly and make sure all passengers are properly secured.
- Do not allow small children to operate the sunroof. Never allow your fingers, other body parts, or any object to project through the sunroof opening. Injury may result.

WIND BUFFETING

- Wind buffeting can be described as a helicopter-type percussion sound. If buffeting occurs with the rear windows open, adjust the front and rear windows together.
- If buffeting occurs with the sunroof open, adjust the sunroof opening, or adjust any window. This will minimize buffeting.

ELECTRONICS

YOUR VEHICLE'S SOUND SYSTEM

Uconnect® Voice Command Button

Uconnect® Phone Button

Next Station or Song

Next Radio Preset

Previous Station or Song

Steering Wheel Audio Controls (left rear surface of steering wheel)

ELECTRONICS

Assist Button

9-1-1 Button

Uconnect® Access 8.4AN Radio

Screen Off

Back Button (Radio Functions)

Volume/Mute Button

Volume Up

Change Audio Source

Volume Down

Steering Wheel Audio Controls (right rear surface of steering wheel)

Tune or Scroll Knob Browse or Enter Button.

Media Hub – may include USB port, SD Card and Audio Jack (inside center console)

Remote Disc Player (in lower center console storage bin, or lower center seat bin) (if equipped)

ELECTRONICS

IDENTIFYING YOUR RADIO

Uconnect® 3.0

- Two hard-keys on either side of the display

Uconnect® 3.0

Uconnect® 5.0

- 5" Touch-Screen
- Three hard-keys on either side of the display

Uconnect® 5.0

Uconnect® 8.4A

- 8.4" Touch-Screen
- Climate soft key in lower menu bar
- HD Button will NOT be visible on right side of screen when viewing AM or FM
- SiriusXM Travel Link feature NOT listed within Apps

Uconnect® 8.4A

Uconnect® 8.4AN

- 8.4" Touch-Screen
- Climate soft key in lower menu bar
- HD Button will be visible on right side of screen when viewing AM or FM
- SiriusXM Travel Link feature listed within Apps

Uconnect® 8.4AN

Uconnect® Access (AVAILABLE ON Uconnect® 8.4A AND Uconnect® 8.4AN) (IF EQUIPPED)

Uconnect® Access enhances your ownership and driving experience by connecting your vehicle with a 3G cellular connection. Uconnect® Access provides:

- The ability to remotely lock/unlock your doors and start your vehicle from virtually anywhere, with the Uconnect® Access App, Owner Connect website and Uconnect® Care (Vehicle must be within the United States and have network coverage).
- The functionality to turn your vehicle into a WiFi Hotspot on demand.
- Theft Alarm Notification via text or email.
- Bing® to help find things, places, businesses and other locations when you need them.
- Voice Texting so you can compose, send and receive text messages with your voice while keeping your hands on the wheel.

Before you drive, familiarize yourself with the easy-to-use Uconnect® System.

1. The ASSIST and 9-1-1 buttons are located on your rearview mirror. The ASSIST Button is used for contacting Roadside Assistance, Vehicle Care and Uconnect® Care. The 9-1-1 Button connects you directly to emergency assistance.

NOTE:

Vehicles sold in Canada and Mexico DO NOT have 9-1-1 Call system capabilities. 9-1-1 or other emergency line operators in Canada and Mexico may not answer or respond to 9-1-1 system calls

2. The Uconnect® "Apps" soft-key on the menu bar at the bottom right corner of the radio touch screen. This is where you can begin your registration process, manage your Apps and purchase WiFi on demand.

ELECTRONICS

3. The Uconnect® Voice Command and Uconnect® Phone buttons are located on the left side of your steering wheel. These buttons let you use your voice to give commands, make phone calls, send and receive text messages hands-free, enter navigation destinations, and control your radio and media devices.

Included Trial Period for New Vehicles

Your new vehicle may come with an included trial period for use of the Uconnect® Access Services starting at the date of vehicle purchase*. To activate the trial, you must first register with Uconnect® Access. Once registered, Uconnect® Access customers can purchase additional Services and Apps over the lifetime of their vehicle ownership.

Features and Packages

After the trial period, you can subscribe to continue your service by visiting the Uconnect® Store located within the Mopar Owner Connect website (MoparOwnerConnect.com). If you need assistance, you can also call Uconnect® Care at 855-792-4241 for U.S. residents and 855-209-8317 for Canadian residents.

For the latest information on packages and pricing information for U.S. residents only, visit www.DriveUconnect.com.

Uconnect® Access Registration

To unlock the full potential of Uconnect® Access in your vehicle, you first need to register with Uconnect® Access.

1. From the parked vehicle with the radio touch screen powered on, select the "Apps" soft-key located near the bottom right-hand corner of the radio touch screen.

NOTE:

Should you require assistance anytime during the registration process, simply press the ASSIST button located on the rear view mirror to be connected with a Uconnect® Care agent.

2. Touch Register on the reminder screen or select the "Uconnect Registration" soft-key which appears in the "Favorites Tab" on the Apps list.

3. The Uconnect® Access Registration App will open and display step-by-step instructions to start your registration.

4. Enter your email address into the radio touch screen.

5. This message will display on the touch screen indicating your email submission was accepted. In a few minutes, you will receive an email which will allow you to register your vehicle for Uconnect® Access. You should open this email and begin your Uconnect® Access registration within 24 hours.

6. A final message will display on the touch screen allowing you to check on the status of your email submission. To exit the registration, press the X in the upper right corner.

NOTE:

For security reasons, this link is valid for 24 hours from the time you submitt your email address into the radio touch screen. If the link has expired, simply re-enter your email address into the Uconnect® Registration App on the radio touch screen to receive another link.

The secured registration link will take you through the Uconnect® Access registration process step by step.

To unlock the full potential of Uconnect® Access in your vehicle, you will need to create or validate an existing Mopar Owner Connect account (previously Owner Center) Uconnect® along with Mopar Owner Connect have joined forces to create one destination to manage all of your vehicle needs- from managing your Uconnect® Access account to tracking service history and finding recommended accessories for your vehicle. If you already have a Mopar Owner Connect account, log in to the website with your existing username and password. For assistance with this web based registration process, call Uconnect® Care at 855-792-4241 for U.S. residents and 855-209-8317 for Canadian residents.

At this point your vehicle is registered with Uconnect® Access. Apps will be downloaded the next time you start your vehicle. It may take over 30 minutes for all of the apps to install. If the apps have not appeared after 24 hours, please contact Uconnect® Care. The recommended next steps are to:

- Set up your Payment Account. (Provides the option to purchase packages and apps, such as WiFi Hotspot)
- Download the Uconnect® Access App. (Allows you to utilize the Remote Services such as Remote Door Unlock)

Download the Uconnect® Access App

If you own a compatible iOS or Android® powered device, the Uconnect Access App allows you to remotely lock or unlock your doors, start your engine or activate your horn and lights from virtually anywhere (Vehicle must be within the United States and have network coverage). You can download the App from Mopar Owner Connect or from the Apple App or Google Play store. FFor Uconnect® Phone customer support and to determing if your device is compatible:

- U.S. residents - visit www.UconnectPhone.com or call 1–877–855–8400
- Canadian residents - call 1–800–465–2001 (English) or 1–800–387–9983 (French)

Purchasing Apps and WiFi

Apps and WiFi can be purchased from the Uconnect® Store within your vehicle, and online at Mopar Owner Connect. You must first register and set up a Uconnect® Access Payment account.

ELECTRONICS

Purchasing Apps and WiFi for your vehicle

1. With the vehicle parked and the radio powered on, select the "Apps" soft-key located near the bottom right-hand corner of the radio touch screen.

2. To launch the Uconnect® Store, select Tools and then select Uconnect® Store.

3. From the Uconnect® Store, select the Application (App) you wish to purchase.

4. This will launch the selected App into purchase mode along with providing additional information. The purchase process begins when you touch the "Buy" soft-key.

5. The Uconnect® Store will display a "Purchase Overview" message confirming the financial details for the App you are about to purchase. Touch the "Purchase" key to continue.

6. The Uconnect® Store will ask you to "Confirm Payment" using your default payment method on file in your Payment Account. Touch the Complete key to continue.

7. The Uconnect® Payment Account will then ask for your "Payment Account PIN". After entering this four digit PIN, touch the Complete key to make the purchase.

8. You will receive a confirmation message that your purchase has been submitted. Touch the OK to end the process.

NOTE:

Purchased apps can take up to 30 minutes to download, depending on your vehicle's cellular coverage at time of purchase. If your download takes more than 30 minutes, please contact Uconnect® Care by pressing the ASSIST button on the rear view mirror.

You can also purchase apps or renew your subscription to a package from the Mopar Owner Connect website. Log In to the Mopar Owner Connect website (www.moparownerconnect.com) with your username and password, and click on the "Store" tab.

Using Uconnect® Access

Getting Started with Apps

Applications (Apps) in your Uconnect® Access system deliver features and services that are customized for the driver and are certified by Chrysler Group, LLC. Two different types are:

• Built-In Apps – **use the built-in 3G Cellular Network on your Uconnect® radio.**

• Brought-In Apps – Uconnect® Access will allow you to use your own smartphone or device's data plan and connection to stream content from Chrysler Group, LLC certified apps into your vehicle and control them using the Uconnect® radio touch-screen, steering wheel controls, and voice recognition.

Get started with your Uconnect® Access apps by pressing the Uconnect® "Apps" soft-key on the menu bar at the bottom right corner of the radio touch screen. Available apps and features are organized by the tabs on the left of the screen.

- Favorite Apps – this is the default screen when you first press the Apps soft-key, and is a good place to put the apps you use most frequently. To make an App a "favorite", press the settings soft-key to the right of the app, and select "Make a favorite".

- Media Apps, Information Apps, and Tools – Organizes your Uconnect® Access apps (when available) into three categories, depending on the type of app.

- Running Apps – press this tab to see which apps are currently running.

Maintaining Your Uconnect® Access Account

Reinstalling an App

You can easily correct many Application related issues you may be experiencing by resetting the App back to the factory setting. From the vehicle's radio touch-screen, complete the following steps:

1. Touch the Uconnect® App and open the Uconnect® Store and go to My Apps.

2. In My Apps, select Settings and then Reinstall App and lastly, Continue.

3. Your Apps have been successfully re-installed.

Canceling Your Subscription

Should you want to cancel your subscription, you can remove your account information using the same procedure contained in the Selling Your Vehicle section.

ELECTRONICS

Selling Your Vehicle

When you sell your vehicle, we recommend that you remove your Uconnect® Access Account information from the vehicle. You can do this using the radio touch screen in the vehicle or on the Mopar Owner Connect website (www.MoparOwnerConnect.com). Removing your account information cancels your subscription and makes your vehicle factory-ready for a new owner/subscriber.

1. From your vehicle's radio touch-screen, select the Uconnect® Store from the Apps icon.

2. Select My apps, then Settings, and then Remove Uconnect® Account.

3. Enter your Uconnect® Security PIN, select "Proceed to Remove Vehicle from Uconnect Account".

For further assistance call Uconnect® Care at 855-792-4241 for U.S. residents and 855-209-8317 for Canadian residents, or visit Mopar Owner Connect (www.MoparOwnerConnect.com) On the Owner Connect site, go to Uconnect® Store, and click on "Remove My Vehicle" button.

In Vehicle Features

1. **Assist Call** – The rear view mirror contains an ASSIST push button which automatically connects the vehicle occupants to one of these predefined destinations for immediate support:

   • **Roadside Assistance Call** – If you get a flat tire, or need a tow, you'll be connected to someone who can help anytime. Additional fees may apply. Additional information in this section.

   • **Uconnect® Access Care** – In vehicle support for Uconnect® Access System, Apps and Features.

   • **Vehicle Care** – Total support for your Chrysler Group LLC vehicle.

2. **Emergency 9-1-1 Call (If Equipped)** – The rear view mirror contains a 9-1-1 button that, when pressed, will place a call to a local 9-1-1 operator to request help from local police, fire or ambulance personnel in the event of an emergency. If this button is accidentally pressed, you will have 10 seconds to cancel the call. To cancel, press the 9-1-1 Call button again or press the cancellation button shown on the touch screen. After 10 seconds has passed, the 9-1-1 call will be placed and only the 9-1-1 operator can cancel it. The LED light on the Rearview Mirror will turn green once a connection to a 9-1-1 operator has been made. The green LED light will turn off once the 9-1-1 call is terminated. Have an authorized dealer service the vehicle if the Rearview Mirror light is continuously red. **If a connection is made between a 9-1-1 operator and your vehicle, you understand and agree that 9-1-1 operators may, like any other 9-1-1 call, record conversations and sounds in and near your vehicle upon connection.**

3. **Roadside Assistance (If Equipped)** - If your vehicle is equipped with this feature and within wireless range, you may be able to connect to Roadside Assistance by

pressing the "Assist" button on the Rearview Mirror. You will be presented with Assist Care options. Make a selection by touching the prompts displayed on the radio If Roadside Assistance is provided to your vehicle, you agree to be responsible for any additional roadside assistance service costs that you may incur. In order to provide Uconnect® Services to you, we may record and monitor your conversations with Roadside Assistance, Uconnect® Care or Vehicle Care, whether such conversations are initiated through the Uconnect® Services in your vehicle, or via a landline or mobile telephone, and may share information obtained through such recording and monitoring in accordance with regulatory requirements. You acknowledge, agree and consent to any recording, monitoring or sharing of information obtained through any such call recordings.

4. **Bing®** - Customers have the ability to search for nearby destinations or a point of interest (POI) either by category or custom search by using keywords (for example, "Italian restaurant"). Searching can be done by voice or using the touch-screen keypad. Using the touch-screen, launch Bing by selecting the Apps icon, touch Information Apps tab, and then touch Bing. Using voice recognition press the VR button on the steering wheel and say "Launch Bing" or just say "Bing" to launch the app.

5. **Theft Alarm Notification** - The Theft Alarm Notification feature notifies you via email or text message (SMS) when the vehicle's factory-installed theft alarm system has been set-off. There are a number of reasons why your alarm may have been triggered, one of which could be that your vehicle was stolen. If so, please see the details of the Stolen Vehicle Assistance service below. When you register, Theft Alarm Notification is automatically set to send you an email at the email address you provide should the alarm go off. You may also opt to have a text message sent to your mobile device.

6. **Stolen Vehicle Assistance** - If your vehicle is stolen, contact local law enforcement immediately to file a stolen vehicle report. Once this report has been filed, Uconnect® care can help locate your vehicle. The Uconnect® Care agent will ask for the stolen vehicle report number issued by local law enforcement. Then, using GPS technology and the built-in wireless connection within your vehicle, the Uconnect® Care agent will be able to locate the stolen vehicle and work with law enforcement to help recover it. (Vehicle must be within the United States, have network coverage and must be registered with Uconnect® Access with an active subscription that includes the applicable feature).

7. **WiFi Hotspot** - WiFi Hotspot is on-demand WiFi 3G connectivity that's built-in and ready to go whenever you are. Once your vehicle is registered for Uconnect® Access, you can purchase a Wifi Hotspot subscription at the Uconnect® Store. After you've made your purchase, turn on your signal and connect your devices. It's never been easier to bring your home or office with you.

Your vehicle must have a working electrical system in order for any of the in vehicle Uconnect® features to operate.

ELECTRONICS

Uconnect® Access Remote Features

If you own a compatible iOS or Android® powered device, the Uconnect® Access App allows you to remotely lock or unlock your doors, start your engine or activate your horn and lights from virtually anywhere (Vehicle must be within the United States and have network coverage). You can download the App from Mopar Owner Connect or from the Apple App or Google Play store. Visit www.UconnectPhone.com to determine if your device is compatible. For Uconnect® Phone customer support and to determing if your device is compatible:

- U.S. residents - visit www.UconnectPhone.com or call 1–877–855–8400
- Canadian residents - call 1–800–465–2001 (English) or 1–800–387–9983 (French)

1. **Remote Start** – This feature provides the ability to start the engine on your vehicle, without the keys and from virtually any distance. You can send a request to your vehicle in one of three ways:

   - Using the Uconnect® Access App from a compatible smartphone
   - From the Mopar Owner Connect website
   - Contacting Uconnect® Care

   You can also send a command to turn-off an engine that has been remote started.

   After 15 minutes if you have not entered your vehicle with the key, the engine will shut off automatically.

   This remote function requires your vehicle to be equipped with a factory-installed Remote Start system. To use this feature after the Uconnect® Access App is downloaded, login with your username and Uconnect® Security PIN.

   You can set-up notifications for your account to receive an email or text (SMS) message every time a command is sent. See the "Managing Notifications" section under Using Mopar Owner Connect (www.MoparOwnerConnect.com) for further instructions.

2. **Remote Door Lock/Unlock** – This feature provides the ability to lock or unlock the door on your vehicle, without the keys and from virtually any distance. You can send a request to your vehicle in one of three ways:

   - Using the Uconnect® Access App from a compatible smartphone
   - From the Mopar Owner Connect website
   - By contacting the Uconnect® Care on the phone

   To use this feature after the Uconnect® Access App is downloaded, login using your username and Uconnect Security PIN. Touch the App button on your smartphone with the closed lock icon to lock the door, and touch the open lock icon to unlock the driver's door.

You can set-up notifications for your account to receive an email or text (SMS) message every time a command is sent. See the "Managing Notifications" section under Using Mopar Owner Connect (www.MoparOwnerConnect.com) for further instructions.

3. **Remote Horn and Lights** – It's easy to locate a vehicle in a dark, crowded or noisy parking area by activating the horn and lights. It may also help if you need to draw attention to your vehicle for any reason. You can send a request to your vehicle in one of three ways:

• Using the Uconnect® Access App from a compatible smartphone

• From the Mopar Owner Connect website

• By contacting the Uconnect® Care on the phone

To use this feature after the Uconnect® Access App is downloaded, login using your username and Uconnect® Security PIN. You can set-up notifications for your account to receive an email or text (SMS) message every time a command is sent. See the "Managing Notifications" section under Using Mopar Owner Connect (www.MoparOwnerConnect.com) for further instructions.

4. **Voice Texting** – Use the sound of your voice to create, listen to and send text messages. Just tell Uconnect® what you want the message to say - it will convert your voice to text and send the message at your command. Powerful, cloud-based voice recognition allows you to dictate free form text messages, and send them from your Bluetooth- enabled phone without taking your hands of the wheel or focus from the road.

ELECTRONICS

WARNING!

- ALWAYS drive safely with your hands on the wheel. You have full responsibility and assume all risks related to the use of the Uconnect® features and applications in this vehicle. Only use Uconnect® when it is safe to do so. Failure to do so may result in an accident involving serious injury or death.
- Ignoring the Rearview Mirror light could mean you may not have 9-1-1 Call service when you need it. If the Rearview Mirror light is illuminated, have an authorized dealer service the 9-1-1 Call system immediately.
- If anyone in the vehicle could be in danger (e.g., fire or smoke is visible, dangerous road conditions or location), do not wait for voice contact from a 9-1-1 operator. All occupants should exit the vehicle immediately and move to a safe location.
- The 9-1-1 Call system is embedded into the vehicle's electrical system. Do not add any aftermarket electrical equipment to the vehicle's electrical system. This may prevent your vehicle from sending a signal to initiate an emergency call. To avoid interference that can cause the 9-1-1 Call system to fail, never add aftermarket equipment (e.g., two-way mobile radio, CB radio, data recorder, etc.) to your vehicle's electrical system or modify the antennas on your vehicle. IF YOUR VEHICLE LOSES BATTERY POWER FOR ANY REASON (INCLUDING DURING OR AFTER AN ACCIDENT), THE UCONNECT® FEATURES, APPS AND SERVICES, AMONG OTHERS, WILL NOT OPERATE.

Uconnect® 3.0

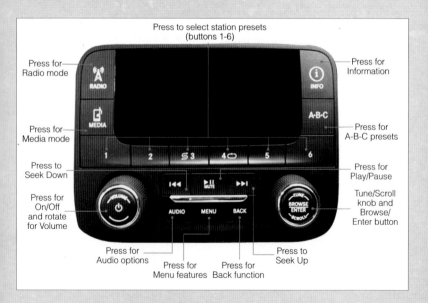

54

Clock Setting

1. Press the Menu button at the bottom of the radio, next select the Time Format setting and then select Set Time.

2. Adjust the hours or minutes by turning the Tune/Scroll knob, then pressing the Enter/Browse button to move to the next entry. You can also select 12hr or 24hr format by turning the Tune/Scroll knob, then pressing the Enter/Browse button on the desired selection.

3. Once the time is set press the "Back" button to exit the time screen.

Audio

- Press the AUDIO button on the radio faceplate.

- The Audio Menu shows the following options for you to customize your audio settings.

Mid, Bass, Fade, Balance

- Select the desired setting to adjust, then touch the Enter/Browse button. Turn the Tune/Scroll knob to adjust the setting + or - 9. Press the back button when done.

Radio Operation

Seek Up/Down Buttons

- Press to seek through radio stations in AM, FM or SXM bands.

- Hold either button to bypass stations without stopping.

Store Radio Presets

- The Presets are available for all Radio Modes, and are activated by touching any of the six Preset buttons.

- When you are receiving a station that you wish to commit into memory, press and hold the desired numbered button for more that 2 seconds or until you hear a confirmation beep.

- The Radio stores up to 18 presets in each of the Radio modes. Press the A-B-C hard-key to select the A, B or C preset list.

Disc Operation

- Your vehicle may have a remote CD player located in the lower center console storage bin, or in the lower center bench seat bin.

- CD/Disc Mode is entered by either inserting a CD/Disc or by touching the Media button located on the side of the display. Once in Media Mode, select Disc.

- Gently insert one CD into the CD player with the CD label facing as indicated on the illustration located on the Disc player.

Seek Up/Down Buttons

- Press to seek through CD tracks.

- Hold either button to bypass tracks without stopping.

ELECTRONICS

USB/Audio Jack (AUX) Operation

USB/iPod®

- USB/iPod® Mode is entered by either inserting a USB Jump Drive or iPod® cable into the USB port or by touching the Media button located left of the display. Once in Media Mode, select USB/iPod for the source.

- Pressing the Media button, then select USB/iPod® to change the mode to the USB device if the device is connected, allowing the music from your portable device to play through the vehicle's speakers.

Audio Jack (AUX)

- The AUX allows a portable device, such as an MP3 player or an iPod®, to be plugged into the radio and utilize the vehicle's audio system, using a 3.5 mm audio cable, to amplify the source and play through the vehicle speakers.

- Pressing the Media button, then touch the source soft-key and then select AUX to change the mode to auxiliary device if the audio jack is connected, allowing the music from your portable device to play through the vehicle's speakers.

- The functions of the portable device are controlled using the device buttons, not the buttons on the radio. The volume may be controlled using the radio or portable device.

Uconnect® 3.0 Available Media Hubs

Uconnect 3.0	Media Hub (USB, AUX Ports)	Media Hub (SD, USB, AUX Ports)	Remote USB Port (Fully Functional)	Remote USB Port (Charging Only)	Dual Charging Ports
	S	-	-	O	O

S = Standard Equipment

O = Optional Equipment

Uconnect® 5.0

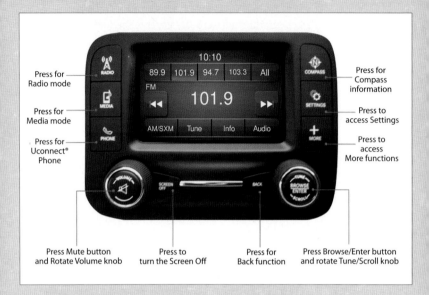

Press for Radio mode

Press for Media mode

Press for Uconnect® Phone

Press for Compass information

Press to access Settings

Press to access More functions

10:10

89.9 101.9 94.7 103.3 All

FM

101.9

AM/SXM Tune Info Audio

Press Mute button and Rotate Volume knob

Press to turn the Screen Off

Press for Back function

Press Browse/Enter button and rotate Tune/Scroll knob

Clock Setting

1. To start the clock setting procedure, perform either of the following:

   • Press the More hard-key on the right side of the display, next press the Time soft-key and then press the Set soft-key.

   • Press the Settings hard-key on the right side of the display, then press the Clock soft-key. The Time setting screen is displayed and the clock can be adjusted as described in the following procedure.

NOTE:

In the Clock Setting Menu you can also select Display Clock. Display Clock turns the clock display in the status bar on or off.

2. Touch the Up or Down arrows to adjust the hours or minutes, next select the AM or PM soft-key. You can also select 12hr or 24hr format by touching the desired soft-key.

3. Once the time is set press the "Done" soft-key to exit the time screen.

ELECTRONICS

Equalizer, Balance and Fade

1. Press the SETTINGS hard-key on the right side of the unit.

2. Then scroll down and press the Audio soft-key to get to the Audio menu.

3. The Audio Menu shows the following options for you to customize your audio settings.

Equalizer

• Touch the Equalizer soft-key to adjust the Bass, Mid and Treble. Use the + or - soft-key to adjust the equalizer to your desired settings. Press the back arrow soft-key when done.

Balance/Fade

• Touch the Balance/Fade soft-key to adjust the sound from the speakers. Use the arrow soft-key to adjust the sound level from the front and rear or right and left side speakers. Touch the Center "C" soft-key to reset the balance and fade to the factory setting. Press the back arrow soft-key when done.

Speed Adjustable

• Touch the Speed Adjusted Volume soft-key to select between OFF, 1, 2 or 3. This will decrease the radio volume relative to a decrease in vehicle speed. Press the back arrow soft-key when done.

Loudness

• Touch the Loudness soft-key to select the Loudness feature. When this feature is activated it improves sound quality at lower volumes.

Radio Operation

Seek Up/Down Buttons

• Press to seek through radio stations in AM, FM or SXM bands.

• Hold either button to bypass stations without stopping.

Store Radio Presets

• When you are receiving a station that you wish to commit into memory, press and hold the desired numbered soft-key for more that 2 seconds or until you hear a confirmation beep.

• The Radio stores up to 12 presets in each of the Radio modes. 4 presets are visible at the top of the radio screen. Touching the "all" soft-key on the radio home screen will display all of the preset stations for that mode.

ELECTRONICS

SiriusXM Premier Over 160 channels

- Get every channel available on your satellite radio, and enjoy all you want, all in one place. Hear commercial-free music plus sports, news, talk and entertainment. Get all the premium programming, including Howard Stern, every NFL game, Oprah Radio®, every MLB® and NHL® game, every NASCAR® race, Martha Stewart and more. And get 20+ Xtra channels, including SiriusXM Latino, a selection of channels dedicated to Spanish language programming.

- To access SiriusXM Satellite Radio, press the "RADIO" hard-key and then the SXM soft-key.

- SiriusXM services require subscriptions, sold separately after the 12-month trial included with the new vehicle purchase. **If you decide to continue your service at the end of your trial subscription, the plan you choose will automatically renew and bill at then-current rates until you call SiriusXM at 1-866-635-2349 for U.S. residents and 1-888-539-7474 for Canadian residents to cancel.** See SiriusXM Customer Agreement for complete terms at www.siriusxm.com. All fees and programming subject to change. Our satellite service is available only to those at least 18 and older in the 48 contiguous USA and D.C. Our Sirius satellite service is also available in PR (with coverage limitations). Our Internet radio service is available throughout our satellite service area and in AK and HI. Visit www.sirius.com/TravelLink for more information on SiriusXM Travel Link.© 2012 Sirius XM Radio Inc. Sirius, XM and all related marks and logos are trademarks of Sirius XM Radio Inc.

Disc Operation

- Your vehicle may have a remote CD player located in the lower center console storage bin, or in the lower center bench seat bin.

- CD/Disc Mode is entered by either inserting a CD/Disc or by touching the Media button located on the side of the display. Once in Media Mode, select Disc.

- Gently insert one CD into the CD player with the CD label facing as indicated on the illustration located on the Disc player.

Seek Up/Down Buttons

- Press to seek through Disc tracks.

- Hold either button to bypass tracks without stopping.

Browse

- Touch the browse soft-key to scroll through and select a desired track on the Disc. Touch the exit soft-key if you wish to cancel the browse function.

USB/Audio Jack (AUX)/Bluetooth® Operation

USB/iPod®

- USB/iPod® Mode is entered by either inserting a USB Jump Drive or iPod® cable into the USB port or by touching the Media hard-key located left of the display. Once in Media Mode, touch the source soft-key and select USB/iPod®

ELECTRONICS

- Pressing the Media hard-key, then touch the source soft-key and then select USB/iPod® to change the mode to the USB device if the device is connected, allowing the music from your portable device to play through the vehicle's speakers.

Audio Jack (AUX)

- The AUX allows a portable device, such as an MP3 player or an iPod®, to be plugged into the radio and utilize the vehicle's audio system, using a 3.5 mm audio cable, to amplify the source and play through the vehicle speakers.

- Pressing the Media hard-key, then touch the source soft-key and then select AUX to change the mode to auxiliary device if the audio jack is connected, allowing the music from your portable device to play through the vehicle's speakers.

- The functions of the portable device are controlled using the device buttons, not the buttons on the radio. The volume may be controlled using the radio or portable device.

Bluetooth®

- Bluetooth® Streaming Audio (BTSA) or Bluetooth® Mode is entered by pairing a Bluetooth® device, containing music, to the Uconnect® Access system.

- Pressing the Media hard-key, then touch the source soft-key and then select Bluetooth® to change the mode to Bluetooth® if the device is paired, allowing the music from your portable device to play through the vehicle's speakers.

Uconnect® 5.0 Available Media Hubs

Uconnect® 5.0	Media Hub (USB, AUX Ports)	Media Hub (SD, USB, AUX Ports)	Remote USB Port (Fully Functional)	Remote USB Port (Charging Only)	Dual Charging Ports
	S	-	-	S	O

S = Standard Equipment

O = Optional Equipment

VOICE COMMAND QUICK REFERENCE

Uconnect® 5.0 Voice Command Quick Reference

- If the Uconnect Voice Command ⦅ᶓ VR button exists on your steering wheel, you have the Voice Command feature, which is optimized for the driver. The Voice Command feature lets you keep your hands on the wheel, and your eyes on the road.

- When you press the Voice Command ⦅ᶓ VR button located on the steering wheel, you will hear a beep. After the beep, give your command. If you do not know what commands to say, you can say "help" and the system will provide options to you. If you ever wish to interrupt the system while it lists options, press the Voice Command ⦅ᶓ VR button, after the beep, say your command.

NOTE:

All phone oriented voice commands are accessible by first pressing the Phone Pick Up ☎ button, not the Voice Command button. To end a call, simply press the Phone Hang Up ☎ button. In some vehicles, the Phone Pickup button serves the dual purpose of ending calls as well.

Voice Command (VR) User TIPs

- To hear available commands, press the Uconnect® Voice Command button and say "Help". You will hear available commands for the menu displayed.

- At any time, you can say the words "Cancel" or "Help". These commands are universal and can be used from virtually any menu. All other specific commands can be used depending upon the active application.

- You can interrupt the system prompts at any time by pressing the Uconnect® Voice Command button while the system is speaking. After the beep, you can say a command.

- You can 'chain' commands together for faster results. Say "Call Joe Doe mobile", for example.

- For best performance, adjust the rearview mirror to provide at least 1/2 in (1 cm) gap between the overhead console (if equipped) and the mirror.

- Always wait for the beep before speaking.

- Speak normally, without pausing, just as you would speak to a person sitting a few feet/meters away from you.

- Make sure that no one other than you is speaking during a Voice Command period.

Steering Wheel Buttons

You can control many of your radio features using your voice. Press either the VR «⸌ VR or Phone Pick Up ☎ button on your steering wheel.

Available Radio Button Voice Commands

	Steering Wheel Buttons to Press:	Radio Mode	Media Mode	Phone Mode
Types of Voice Commands Available	Uconnect® Voice Command (VR) Button	AM/FM & Satellite Brand Control	Media Devices Control	-
		GENERAL		
	Uconnect® Phone Pick Up Button	-	-	Call Initiation, Call Management, Pre-formatted Voice Text Reply

ELECTRONICS

Voice Command Examples – Uconnect® 5.0

GENERAL	
Anytime	"Go to Radio" (Media, Phone) – Compass, Settings, and More functions are not Voice Command accessible "Cancel" "Help" (to listen to suggested commands specific to current need "Repeat"

RADIO	
AM/FM	"Tune to AM950", "Tune to 95.5FM (preset 5)
Satellite Band Control	"Tune to Satellite Channel 80's on 8", Tune to Satellite Channel 32 (preset 4)

MEDIA	
Media Devices Control (Functionality is dependent on compatibility between devises and radio)	"Browse" (show) "artist" (albums, music) "Show paired phones" (devices) "Play song – Maple Leaf Rag" (artist - Scott Joplin, genre - rock, album - Ragtime Favorites)

PHONE	
Call Initiation (Requires that phone has been Bluetooth® paired with radio	"Dial 123-456-7890" (phone number) "Call John Smith mobile" (home, office, other) "Redial" "Show outgoing" (recent) "calls"
Call Management	"Search for John Smith" (any contact name in address book) "Show (display list) contacts"

Voice Text Reply (Radio audibly recognizes these 18 pre-formatted SMS messages as you speak)	Forward one of 18 pre-formatted SMS messages to incoming calls/text messages: "Yes." "No." "Okay." "I can't talk right now." "Call me." "I'll call you later." "I'm on my way." "Thanks." "I'll be late." "I will be <number> minutes late." "See you in <number> minutes" "Stuck in traffic." "Start without me." "Where are you?" "Are you there yet?" "I need directions." "I'm lost." "See you later."

Uconnect® 8.4A

Uconnect® 8.4A AT A GLANCE

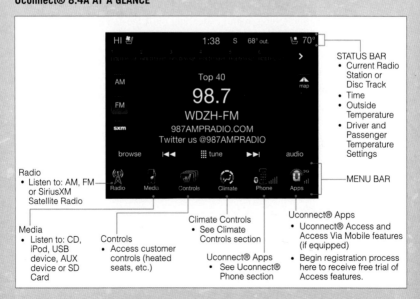

ELECTRONICS

Displaying the Time

- If the time is not currently displayed on the radio or player main page, touch the Settings soft-key or the Apps soft-key and then the Settings soft-key. In the Settings list, touch the Clock soft-key then touch the check box next to Show Time in Status Bar.

Setting the Time

- Model 8.4AN synchronizes time automatically via GPS, so should not require any time adjustment. If you do need to set the time manually, follow the instructions below for Model 8.4A.

- For Model 8.4A, turn the unit on, then touch the time display at the top of the screen. Touch Yes.

- If the time is not displayed at the top of the screen, touch the Settings soft-key or the Apps soft-key and then the Settings soft-key. In the Settings screen, touch the Clock soft-key, then check or uncheck this option.

- Touch + or – next to Set Time Hours and Set Time Minutes to adjust the time.

- If these features are not available, uncheck the Sync with GPS box.

- Touch X to save your settings and exit out of the Clock Setting screen.

Audio Settings

- Touch of the Audio soft-key to activate the Audio settings screen to adjust Balance\Fade, Equalizer, and Speed Adjusted Volume.

- You can return to the Radio screen by touching the X located at the top right.

Balance/Fade

- Touch the Balance/Fade soft-key to Balance audio between the front speakers or fade the audio between the rear and front speakers.

- Touching the Front, Rear, Left, or Right soft-keys or touch and drag the blue Speaker Icon to adjust the Balance/Fade.

Equalizer

- Touch the Equalizer soft-key to activate the Equalizer screen.

- Touch the + or - soft-keys, or by touching and dragging over the level bar for each of the equalizer bands. The level value, which spans between plus or minus 9, is displayed at the bottom of each of the Bands.

Speed Adjusted Volume

- Touch the Speed Adjusted Volume soft-key to activate the Speed Adjusted Volume screen. The Speed Adjusted Volume is adjusted by touching the + and - buttons or by touching and dragging over the level bar. This alters the automatic adjustment of the audio volume with variation to vehicle speed.

ELECTRONICS

RADIO

- To access the Radio mode, touch the Radio soft-key at the lower left of the screen.

Selecting Radio Stations

- Touch the desired radio band (AM, FM or SXM) soft-key.

Seek Up/Seek Down

- Touch the Seek arrow soft-keys for less than two seconds to seek through radio stations.

- Touch and hold either arrow soft-key for more than two seconds to bypass stations without stopping. The radio will stop at the next listenable station once the arrow soft-key is released.

Direct Tune

- Tune directly to a radio station by pressing the Tune soft-key on the screen, and entering the desired station number.

Store Radio Presets

- Your radio can store 12 total preset stations. They are shown at the top of your screen. To see all 12 stations, press the arrow soft-key at the top right of the screen to toggle between the six presets.

- To set a station into memory press and hold the desired numbered soft-key for more than two seconds or until you hear a confirmation beep.

ELECTRONICS

SiriusXM PREMIER OVER 160 CHANNELS

- Get every channel available on your satellite radio, and enjoy all you want, all in one place. Hear commercial-free music plus sports, news, talk and entertainment. Get all the premium programming, including Howard Stern, every NFL game, Oprah Radio®, every MLB® and NHL® game, every NASCAR® race, Martha Stewart and more. And get 20+ Xtra channels, including SiriusXM Latino, a selection of channels dedicated to Spanish language programming.

- To access SiriusXM Satellite Radio, touch the SXM soft-key on the main Radio screen.

- The following describes features that are available when in SiriusXM Satellite Radio mode.

Seek Up/Seek Down

- Touch the Seek arrow soft-keys for less than two seconds to seek through channels in SXM mode.

- Touch and hold either arrow soft-key for more than two seconds to bypass channels without stopping. The radio will stop at the next listenable channel once the arrow soft-key is released.

Direct Tune

- Tune directly to a SXM channel by pressing the Tune soft-key on the screen, and entering the desired station number.

Jump

- Automatically tells you when Traffic & Weather for a favorite city is available, and gives you the option to switch to that channel. Touch Jump to activate the feature. After listening to Traffic and Weather, touch Jump again to return to the previous channel.

Fav

- Activates the favorites menu. You can add up to 50 favorite artists or songs. Just touch Add Fav Artist or Add Fav Song while the song is playing. You will then be alerted any time one of these songs, or works by these artists, is playing on other SiriusXM channels.

SiriusXM Parental Controls

- You can skip or hide certain channels from view if you do not want access to them. Touch the More soft-key, then the Settings soft-key, next touch the Sirius Setup soft-key, then select Channel Skip. Touch the box, check-mark, next to the channel you want skipped. They will not show up in normal usage.

- SiriusXM also offers the option to permanently block selected channels. Call (1-888-601-6297 for U.S. customers, 1-888-539-7474 for Canadian customers) and request the Family Package.

ELECTRONICS

Browse

- Lets you browse the SiriusXM channel listing or Genre listing. Favorites, Game Zone, Weather and Jump settings also provide a way to browse the SiriusXM channel list.

Browse Sub-Menu	Sub-Menu Description
All	Shows the channel listing.
Genre	Provides a list of all genres, and lets you jump to a channel within the selected genre.
Presets	Lets you scroll the list of Preset satellite channels. Touch the channel, or press Enter on the Tune knob, to go to that channel. Touch the trash can icon to delete a preset. Your presets are also shown at the top of the main Satellite Radio screen.
Favorites	Lets you manage artists and songs in the Favorites list and configure Alert Settings to let you know when favorite songs or artists are playing on other channels. Also, view a list of channels airing any of your Favorites.
Game Zone	Provides alerts when your favorite sports teams are starting a game which is being aired on other SiriusXM channels, or when their game score is announced. You can select and manage your Teams list here, and configure alerts.
Jump	Lets you select your favorite cities for Traffic & Weather information, which is used by the Jump feature on the main satellite radio screen.

Replay

- Lets you replay up to 44 minutes of the content of the current SiriusXM channel.

Replay Option	Option Description
Play/Pause	Touch to Pause content playback. Touch Pause/Play again to resume playback.
Rewind/RW	Rewinds the channel content in steps of 5 seconds. Touch and hold to rewind continuously, then release to begin playing content at that point.
Fast Forward/FW	Forwards the content, and works similarly to Rewind/RW. However, Fast Forward/FW can only be used when content has been previously rewound.
Replay Time	Displays the amount of time in the upper center of the screen by which your content lags the Live channel.
Live	Resumes playback of Live content at any time while replaying rewound content.

- SiriusXM services require subscriptions, sold separately after the 12-month trial included with the new vehicle purchase. **If you decide to continue your service at the end of your trial subscription, the plan you choose will automatically renew and bill at then-current rates until you call SiriusXM at 1-866-635-2349 for U.S. residents and 1-888-539-7474 for Canadian residents to cancel.** See SiriusXM Customer Agreement for complete terms at www.siriusxm.com. All fees and programming subject to change. Our satellite service is available only to those at least 18 and older in the 48 contiguous USA and D.C. Our Sirius satellite service is also available in PR (with coverage limitations). Our Internet radio service is available throughout our satellite service area and in AK and HI. Visit www.sirius.com/TravelLink for more information on SiriusXM Travel Link.© 2012 Sirius XM Radio Inc. Sirius, XM and all related marks and logos are trademarks of Sirius XM Radio Inc.

Disc Operation

- Your vehicle may have a remote CD player located in the lower center console storage bin, or in the lower center bench seat bin.
- CD/Disc Mode is entered by either inserting a CD/Disc or by touching the Media button located on the side of the display. Once in Media Mode, select Disc.
- Gently insert one CD into the CD player with the CD label facing as indicated on the illustration located on the Disc player.

Seek Up/Down Buttons

- Press to seek through Disc tracks.
- Hold either button to bypass tracks without stopping.

Browse

- Touch the browse soft-key to scroll through and select a desired track on the Disc. Touch the exit soft-key if you wish to cancel the browse function.

MEDIA HUB – PLAYING iPod/USB/MP3 DEVICES

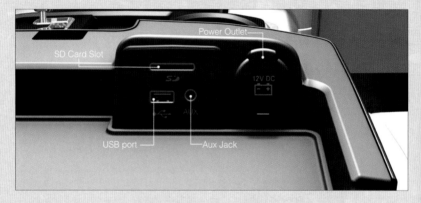

- There are many ways to play music from iPod®/MP3 players or USB devices through your vehicle's sound system.

Audio Jack (AUX)

- The AUX allows a portable device, such as an MP3 player or an iPod®, to be plugged into the radio and utilize the vehicle's sound system, using a 3.5 mm audio cable, to amplify the source and play through the vehicle speakers.

ELECTRONICS

- Touching the Media soft-key then choosing AUX source will change the mode to auxiliary device if the audio jack is connected, allowing the music from your portable device to be heard through the vehicle's speakers. In order to activate the AUX, plug in the audio jack.

- The functions of the portable device are controlled using the device buttons. The volume may be controlled using the radio or portable device.

- To route the audio cable out of the center console, use the access cut out in the front of the console.

USB Port

- Connect your iPod® or compatible device using a USB cable into the USB Port. USB Memory sticks with audio files can also be used. Then, audio from the device can be played on the vehicles sound system while providing metadata (artist, track title, album, etc.) information on the radio display.

- When connected, the iPod®/compatible USB device can be controlled using the radio or Steering Wheel Audio Controls to play, skip to the next or previous track, browse, and list the contents.

- The iPod® battery charges when plugged into the USB port (if supported by the specific device).

- To route the USB/iPod® cable out of the center console, use the access cut out.

NOTE:

- When connecting your iPod® device for the first time, the system may take several minutes to read your music, depending on the number of files. For example, the system will take approximately 5 minutes for every 1000 songs loaded on the device. Also during the reading process, the Shuffle and Browse functions will be disabled. This process is needed to ensure the full use of your iPod® features and only happens the first time it is connected. After the first time, the reading process of your iPod® will take considerably less time unless changes are made or new songs are added to the playlist.

- The USB port supports certain Mini, Classic, Nano, Touch, and iPhone® devices. The USB port also supports playing music from compatible external USB Mass Storage Class memory devices. Some iPod® software versions may not fully support the USB port features. Please visit Apple's website for iPod® software updates.

SD Card

- Play songs stored on an SD card inserted into the SD card slot.

- Song playback can be controlled using the radio or Steering Wheel Audio Controls to play, skip to the next or previous track, browse, and list the contents.

ELECTRONICS

Bluetooth® Streaming Audio

- If equipped with Uconnect® Voice Command, your Bluetooth-equipped iPod® devices, cell phones or other media players, may also be able to stream music to your vehicle's sound system. Your connected device must be Bluetooth-compatible, and paired with your system (see Uconnect® Phone for pairing instructions). You can access the music from your connected Bluetooth® device by touching the Bluetooth® soft-key while in Media mode.

Uconnect® 8.4A & 8.4AN Available Media Hubs

Uconnect® 8.4A & 8.4AN	Media Hub (USB, AUX Ports)	Media Hub (SD, USB, AUX Ports)	Remote USB Port (Fully Functional)	Remote USB Port (Charging Only)	Dual Charging Ports
	-	S	S	O	O

S = Standard Equipment

O = Optional Equipment

iPod®/CD/AUX CONTROLS

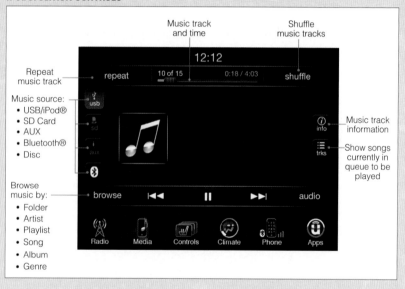

- The iPod®/CD/AUX controls are accessed by touching the desired soft-key displayed on the side of the screen and choosing between Disc, AUX, iPod®, Bluetooth or SD Card.

NOTE:
Uconnect® Access will usually automatically switch to the appropriate mode when something is first connected or inserted into the system.

NAVIGATION (DEALER-INSTALLED OPTION)

- Your Uconnect® 8.4A is "Navigation-Ready", and can be equipped with Navigation at an extra cost. See your dealer for details.
- The information in this section is only applicable if the feature has been equipped. If so equipped, you will see a Nav soft-key at the bottom of the touch-screen.

Changing the Navigation Voice Prompt Volume

1. Touch the View Map soft-key from the Nav Main Menu.
2. With the map displayed, touch the Settings soft-key in the lower right area of the screen.
3. In the Settings menu, touch the Guidance soft-key.
4. In the Guidance menu, adjust the Nav Volume by touching the + or – soft-keys.

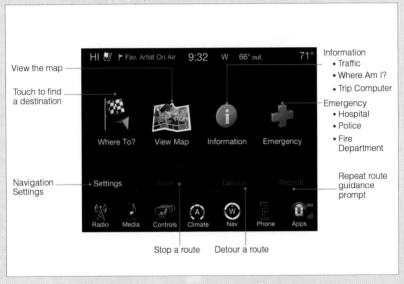

Finding Points of Interest

- From the main Navigation menu, touch Where To? soft-key, then touch the Points of Interest soft-key.
- Select a Category and then a subcategory, if necessary.
- Select your destination and touch the Yes soft-key.

ELECTRONICS

Finding a Place by Spelling the Name

- From the Main Navigation Menu, touch Where to? soft-key, then touch the Points of Interest soft-key and then touch the Spell Name soft-key.
- Enter the name of your destination.
- Touch the Done soft-key.
- Select your destination and touch the Yes soft-key.

Entering a Destination Address

- From the main Navigation menu, touch Where To? soft-key, then touch the Address soft-key.
- Follow the on-screen prompts to enter the address and touch the Yes soft-key.
- Destination entry is not available while your vehicle is in motion. However, you can also use Voice Command to enter an address while moving. See Voice Command Tips for more information.

Setting Your Home Location

- Touch the NAV soft-key in the menu bar to access the Navigation system and the Main Navigation menu.
- Touch Where To? soft-key, then touch the Go Home soft-key.
- You may enter your address directly, use your current location as your home address, or choose from recently found locations.
- To delete your Home location (or other saved locations) so you can save a new Home location, touch the Where To? soft-key from the Main Navigation menu, then touch the Go Home soft-key, and in the Yes screen touch the Options soft-key. In the Options menu touch Clear Home. Set a new Home location by following the previous instructions.

Go Home

- A Home location must be saved in the system. From the Main Navigation menu, touch Where To? soft-key, then touch the Go Home soft-key.

Next turn street – Touch to view Turn List

Distance to next turn

Estimated time of arrival – Touch to change data field

Zoom in and out

Your location on the map

Touch for Nav Main Me

Navigation Routing Options

Current street location

- Your route is marked with a blue line on the map. If you depart from the original route, your route is recalculated. A speed limit icon could appear as you travel on major roadways.

Adding a Stop

- To add a stop you must be navigating a route.
- Touch the Menu soft-key to return to the Main Navigation menu.
- Touch Where To? soft-key, then search for the extra stop. When another location has been selected, you can choose to cancel your previous route, add as the first destination or add as the last destination.
- Touch the desired selection and touch the Yes soft-key.

Taking a Detour

- To take a detour you must be navigating a route.
- Touch the Detour soft-key.

NOTE:

- If the route you are currently taking is the only reasonable option, the device might not calculate a detour.
- For more information, see your Uconnect® Access User's Manual.

ELECTRONICS

Uconnect® Phone (Bluetooth® HANDS FREE CALLING)

- If the Uconnect® Phone Button 📞 exists on your steering wheel, then you have the Uconnect® Phone features.

- The Uconnect® Phone is a voice-activated, hands-free, in-vehicle communications system with Voice Command Capability (see Voice Command section).

- The Uconnect® Phone allows you to dial a phone number with your mobile phone using simple voice commands or using screen soft-keys.

- Refer to the Understand The Features Of Your Vehicle section of your vehicle's Owner's Manual on the DVD for further details.

NOTE:

The Uconnect® Phone requires a mobile phone equipped with the Bluetooth® Hands-Free Profile, Version 1.0 or higher. For Uconnect® Customer Support: U.S. residents visit www.UconnectPhone.com or call 1–877–855–8400. Canadian Residents call, 1-800-465–2001 (English) or 1-800-387-9983 (French).

Pairing a Phone

- To use the Uconnect® Phone feature, you must first pair your Bluetooth® phone with the Uconnect® system.

Start pairing procedure on the radio

- Touch the Phone soft-key and then the Settings soft-key. Next, touch Add Device.

- Uconnect® Phone will display an "In progress" screen while the system is connecting.

Start pairing procedure on mobile phone

- Search for available devices on your Bluetooth® enabled mobile phone. This is usually within Settings or Options under "Bluetooth". See your mobile phone's manual for details.

- When your phone finds the system, select "Uconnect" as the paired device. You may be prompted by your phone to download the phonebook. This is so you can make calls by saying the name of your contact (PBAP-Phone Book Access Profile).

Complete the pairing procedure

- When prompted on the phone, enter the 4-digit PIN number shown on the Uconnect® Screen.

- If your phone asks you to accept a connection request from Uconnect, select "Yes". If available, check the box telling it not to ask again – that way your phone will automatically connect each time you start the vehicle.

Select the mobile phone's priority level

- When the pairing process has successfully completed, the system will prompt you to choose whether or not this is your favorite phone. Selecting Yes will make this phone the highest priority. This phone will take precedence over other paired phones within range. Only one phone can be paired at a time.

- You are now ready to make hands-free calls. Press the Uconnect® Phone button on your steering wheel to begin.

Making A Phone Call

- Press the Uconnect® Phone button 📞 .
- (After the BEEP), say "dial" then the number (or "call" then the name as listed in your phone; see Phonebook).

NOTE:
You can also initiate a call by using the touch-screen on the Phone main screen.

Receiving A Call – Accept (And End)

- When an incoming call rings/is announced on Uconnect®, press the Phone button 📞 .
- To end a call, press the Phone button 📞 .

Mute (Or Unmute) Microphone During Call

- During a call, touch the mute soft-key on the Phone main screen to mute and unmute the call.

Transfer Ongoing Call Between Handset And Vehicle

- During a call, touch the Transfer soft-key on the Phone main screen to transfer an on-going call between handset and vehicle.

Common Phone Commands (Examples)

- "Call John Smith"
- "Call John Smith mobile"
- "Dial 1 248 555 1212
- "Call Emergency"
- "Call Towing Assistance"
- "Redial"

Phonebook

- Uconnect® radios will automatically download your phonebook from your paired phone, if this feature is supported by your phone. Entries are updated each time that the phone is connected. If your phone book entries do not appear, check the settings on your phone. Some phones require you to enable this feature manually.
- Your phonebook can be browsed on your radio screen, but editing can only be done on your phone. To browse, touch the Phone soft-key, then the Phonebook soft-key.
- Favorite phonebook entries can be saved as Favorites for quicker access. Favorites are shown at the top of your main phone screen.

ELECTRONICS

Voice Command Tips

- Using complete names (i.e; Call John Doe vs. Call John) will result in greater system accuracy.
- You can "chain" commands together for faster results. Say "Call John Doe, mobile", for example.
- If you are listening to available voice command options, you do not have to listen to the entire list. When you hear the command that you need, press the (« VR button on the steering wheel, wait for the beep and say your command.

Changing The Volume Of The Voice Command Prompts

- Start a dialogue by pressing the Phone button 📞 , then say a command, for example - "Help".
- Use the radio ON/OFF VOLUME rotary knob to adjust the Uconnect™ audio prompt volume to a comfortable level. Please note that the Uconnect™ audio prompt volume setting for Uconnect™ is different than the audio system.

NOTE:

To access help, press the Uconnect™ Phone 📞 button on the steering wheel and say "help." Touch the display or push either 📞 or (« VR button and say "cancel" to cancel the help session.

Voice Texting

- Voice texting enhances the voice text reply feature built into your Uconnect 8.4A and Uconnect 8.4AN radio, and helps reduce driver distraction while keeping you connected. While voice text reply provides 18 pre-formatted messages you can send, voice texting lets you create and send nearly any message you want. Just speak your message as if you were talking to the recipient, and the Uconnect Access voice-to-text technology will convert your voice into a text message. Voice texting and voice text reply features are compatible with many newer Android and Blackberry phones. Before using, determine if your phone has been tested to support Bluetooth 'Message Access Protocol" (MAP) or AT Messaging Protocol at www.UconnectPhone.com, and ensure MAP is on and incoming message notification is enabled.
- Uconnect® Phone can read or send new text messages on your mobile phone.
- Your mobile phone must support SMS over Bluetooth® in order to use this feature. If the Uconnect® Phone determines your phone is not compatible with SMS messaging over Bluetooth® the "Messaging" button will be greyed out and the feature will not be available for use.

NOTE:

- For mobile phone compatibility and pairing instructions, please visit www.UconnectPhone.com
- Uconnect® Phone SMS touch-screen input is only available when the vehicle is not moving.

WARNING!

- Any voice commanded system should be used only in safe driving conditions following applicable laws regarding phone use. Your attention should be focused on safely operating the vehicle. Failure to do so may result in a collision causing you and others to be severely injured or killed.
- In an emergency, to use Uconnect® Phone, your mobile phone must be:
  - turned on,
  - paired to Uconnect® Phone,
  - and have network coverage.

VOICE COMMAND QUICK REFERENCE

Uconnect® 8.4A Voice Command Quick Reference

- If the Uconnect® Voice Command ⟨⟨ξ VR button exists on your steering wheel, you have the Voice Command feature, which is optimized for the driver. The Voice Command feature lets you keep your hands on the wheel, and your eyes on the road.

- When you press the Voice Command ⟨⟨ξ VR button located on the steering wheel, you will hear a beep. After the beep, give your command. If you do not know what commands to say, you can say "help" and the system will provide options to you. If you ever wish to interrupt the system while it lists options, press the Voice Command ⟨⟨ξ VR button, after the beep, say your command.

NOTE:

All phone oriented voice commands are accessible by first pressing the Phone Pick Up ✆ button, not the Voice Command button. To end a call, simply press the Phone Hang Up ☎ button. In some vehicles, the Phone Pickup ✆ button serves the dual purpose of ending calls as well.

Voice Command (VR) User TIPs

- To hear available commands, press the Uconnect® Voice Command button and say "Help". You will hear available commands for the menu displayed.

- At any time, you can say the words "Cancel" or "Help". These commands are universal and can be used from virtually any menu. All other specific commands can be used depending upon the active application.

- You can interrupt the system prompts at any time by pressing the Uconnect® Voice Command button while the system is speaking. After the beep, you can say a command.

- You can 'chain' commands together for faster results. Say "Call Joe Doe mobile", for example.

- For best performance, adjust the rearview mirror to provide at least 1/2 in (1 cm) gap between the overhead console (if equipped) and the mirror.

- Always wait for the beep before speaking.

ELECTRONICS

- Speak normally, without pausing, just as you would speak to a person sitting a few feet/meters away from you.
- Make sure that no one other than you is speaking during a Voice Command period.

Steering Wheel Buttons

- You can control many of your radio features using your voice. Press either the VR «⟨ VR or Phone Pick Up ☎ button on your steering wheel.

Available Radio Soft–Key Voice Commands

Types of Voice Commands Available	Steering Wheel Buttons to Press:	(1)Radio Mode	(2)Media Mode	(3)Climate Controls	(4)Navigation	(5)Phone Mode	(6)APPS
	Uconnect® Voice Command (VR) Button	AM/FM & Satellite Brand Control	Media Devices Control	Temperature Control	Destination Selection and View	-	BING
		GENERAL					
	Uconnect® Phone Pick Up Button	-	-	-	-	Call Initiation, Call Management, Pre-formatted Voice Text Reply	-

ELECTRONICS

Voice Command Examples – Uconnect® 8.4A

GENERAL	
Anytime	"Go to Radio" (Media, Climate, Navigation, Phone, Apps) – Settings, and Controls are not Voice Command accessible "Cancel" "Help" (to listen to suggested commands specific to current need "Repeat" "Launch BING" – Required 1st voice command to launch BING app "BING Search" – Required 2nd voice command to activate app functionality using Steering Wheel Voice Control Button

RADIO	
AM/FM	"Tune to AM950", "Tune to 95.5FM (preset 5)
Satellite Band Control	"Tune to Satellite Channel 80's on 8", Tune to Satellite Channel 32 (preset 4)

MEDIA	
Media Devices Control (Functionality is dependent on compatibility between devises and radio)	"Browse" (show) "artist" (albums, music) "Show paired phones" (devices) "Play song – Maple Leaf Rag" (artist - Scott Joplin, genre - rock, album - Ragtime Favorites) "Shuffle" – available with iPod, USB and SD Card

CLIMATE	
Temperature Control	"Set temperature to 70 degrees" – single climate zone vehicles
	"Set driver" (passenger) "temperature to 75 degrees" – dual climate zone vehicles

NAVIGATION	
Destination Selection & View	"Enter address" (provide location inputs sequentially, via audible radio prompts) "Go Home" – destination previously defined by driver "Repeat guidance" – hear the last navigation prompt "Cancel Route" "View Map"

PHONE	
Call Initiation (Requires that phone has been Bluetooth® paired with radio	"Dial 123-456-7890" (phone number) "Call John Smith mobile" (home, office, other) "Redial" "Show outgoing" (recent) "calls"
Call Management	"Search for John Smith" (any contact name in address book) "Show (display list) contacts"

Voice Texting (Available during trial period or if subscribed to Uconnect® Access Advantage)	Create a text message using Voice Command Capability "Send a message to John Smith (123-456-7890)" "Show Messages" "Listen to" (view) "number 4" "Forward text" (message) "to John Smith" (phone type, number)
Voice Text Reply (Radio audibly recognizes these 18 pre-formatted SMS messages as you speak)	Forward one of 18 pre-formatted SMS messages to incoming calls/text messages: "Yes." "No." "Okay." "I can't talk right now." "Call me." "I'll call you later." "I'm on my way." "Thanks." "I'll be late." "I will be <number> minutes late." "See you in <number> minutes" "Stuck in traffic." "Start without me." "Where are you?" "Are you there yet?" "I need directions." "I'm lost." "See you later."
APPS	
BING (BING adds it's own audible prompts, and response time varies depending on carrier coverage speed)	"Launch BING" – Required 1st voice command to launch BING app "BING Search" – Required 2nd voice command to activate app functionality using Steering Wheel Voice Control Button "Hotel" (restaurant, gas station, mail, hospital) – for nearest desired general POI "Italian restaurants" – for nearest specified POI category "Hotels" (restaurants, hospitals, Starbucks) "in Miami" (location) – specified distance POI

ELECTRONICS

Uconnect® 8.4AN

Uconnect® 8.4AN AT A GLANCE

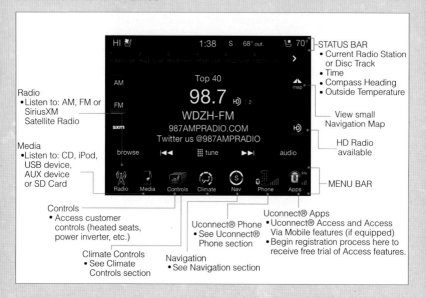

Radio
• Listen to: AM, FM or SiriusXM Satellite Radio

Media
• Listen to: CD, iPod, USB device, AUX device or SD Card

Controls
• Access customer controls (heated seats, power inverter, etc.)

Climate Controls
• See Climate Controls section

Navigation
• See Navigation section

Uconnect® Phone
• See Uconnect® Phone section

STATUS BAR
• Current Radio Station or Disc Track
• Time
• Compass Heading
• Outside Temperature

View small Navigation Map

HD Radio available

MENU BAR

Uconnect® Apps
• Uconnect® Access and Access Via Mobile features (if equipped)
• Begin registration process here to receive free trial of Access features.

Displaying the Time

• If the time is not currently displayed on the radio or player main page, touch the Settings soft-key or the Apps soft-key and then the Settings soft-key. In the Settings list, touch the Clock soft-key then touch the check box next to Show Time in Status Bar.

Setting the Time

• Model 8.4AN synchronizes time automatically via GPS, so should not require any time adjustment. If you do need to set the time manually, follow the instructions below for Model 8.4A.

• For Model 8.4A, turn the unit on, then touch the time display at the top of the screen. Touch Yes.

• If the time is not displayed at the top of the screen, touch Settings soft-key or the Apps soft-key and then the Settings soft-key. In the Settings screen, touch the Clock soft-key, then check or uncheck this option.

• Touch + or – next to Set Time Hours and Set Time Minutes to adjust the time.

• If these features are not available, uncheck the Sync with GPS box.

• Touch X to save your settings and exit out of the Clock Setting screen.

Audio Settings

- Touch of the Audio soft-key to activate the Audio settings screen to adjust Balance\Fade, Equalizer, and Speed Adjusted Volume.
- You can return to the Radio screen by touching the X located at the top right.

Balance/Fade

- Touch the Balance/Fade soft-key to Balance audio between the front speakers or fade the audio between the rear and front speakers.
- Touching the Front, Rear, Left, or Right soft-keys or touch and drag the blue Speaker Icon to adjust the Balance/Fade.

Equalizer

- Touch the Equalizer soft-key to activate the Equalizer screen.
- Touch the + or - soft-keys, or by touching and dragging over the level bar for each of the equalizer bands. The level value, which spans between plus or minus 9, is displayed at the bottom of each of the Bands.

Speed Adjusted Volume

- Touch the Speed Adjusted Volume soft-key to activate the Speed Adjusted Volume screen. The Speed Adjusted Volume is adjusted by touching the + and - buttons or by touching and dragging over the level bar. This alters the automatic adjustment of the audio volume with variation to vehicle speed.

RADIO

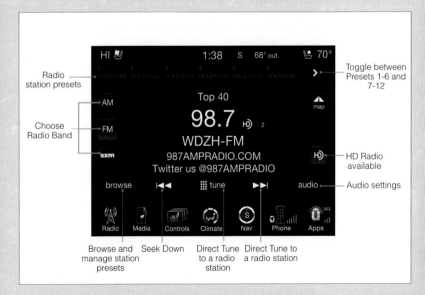

ELECTRONICS

- To access the Radio mode, touch the Radio soft-key at the lower left of the screen.

Selecting Radio Stations

- Touch the desired radio band (AM, FM or SXM) soft-key.

Seek Up/Seek Down

- Touch the Seek arrow soft-keys for less than two seconds to seek through radio stations.
- Touch and hold either arrow soft-key for more than two seconds to bypass stations without stopping. The radio will stop at the next listenable station once the arrow soft-key is released.

Direct Tune

- Tune directly to a radio station by pressing the "Tune" button on the screen, and entering the desired station number.

Store Radio Presets

- Your radio can store 12 total preset stations. They are shown at the top of your screen. To see all 12 stations, press the arrow soft-key at the top right of the screen to toggle between the six presets.
- To set a station into memory press and hold the desired numbered soft-key for more than two seconds or until you hear a confirmation beep.

HD Radio

- HD Radio technology (available on Uconnect 8.4AN) operates similar to conventional radio except it allows broadcasters to transmit a high-quality digital signal.
- With an HD radio receiver, the listener is provided with a clear sound that enhances the listening experience. HD radio can also transmit data such as song title or artist.

SiriusXM PREMIER OVER 160 CHANNELS

- Get every channel available on your satellite radio, and enjoy all you want, all in one place. Hear commercial-free music plus sports, news, talk and entertainment. Get all the premium programming, including Howard Stern, every NFL game, Oprah Radio®, every MLB® and NHL® game, every NASCAR® race, Martha Stewart and more. And get 20+ Xtra channels, including SiriusXM Latino, a selection of channels dedicated to Spanish language programming.
- To access SiriusXM Satellite Radio, touch the SXM soft-key on the main Radio screen.
- The following describes features that are available when in SiriusXM Satellite Radio mode.

Seek Up/Seek Down

- Touch the Seek arrow soft-keys for less than two seconds to seek through channels in SXM mode.

- Touch and hold either arrow soft-key for more than two seconds to bypass channels without stopping. The radio will stop at the next listenable channel once the arrow soft-key is released.

Direct Tune

- Tune directly to a SXM channel by pressing the Tune soft-key on the screen, and entering the desired station number.

Jump

- Automatically tells you when Traffic & Weather for a favorite city is available, and gives you the option to switch to that channel. Touch Jump to activate the feature. After listening to Traffic and Weather, touch Jump again to return to the previous channel.

Fav

- Activates the favorites menu. You can add up to 50 favorite artists or songs. Just touch Add Fav Artist or Add Fav Song while the song is playing. You will then be alerted any time one of these songs, or works by these artists, is playing on other SiriusXM channels.

SiriusXM Parental Controls

- You can skip or hide certain channels from view if you do not want access to them. Touch the More soft-key, then the Settings soft-key, next touch the Sirius Setup soft-key, then select Channel Skip. Touch the box, check-mark, next to the channel you want skipped. They will not show up in normal usage.
- SiriusXM also offers the option to permanently block selected channels. Call (1-888-601-6297 for U.S. customers, 1-888-539-7474 for Canadian customers) and request the Family Package.

Browse

- Lets you browse the SiriusXM channel listing or Genre listing. Favorites, Game Zone, Weather and Jump settings also provide a way to browse the SiriusXM channel list.

Browse Sub-Menu	Sub-Menu Description
All	Shows the channel listing.
Genre	Provides a list of all genres, and lets you jump to a channel within the selected genre.
Presets	Lets you scroll the list of Preset satellite channels. Touch the channel, or press Enter on the Tune knob, to go to that channel. Touch the trash can icon to delete a preset. Your presets are also shown at the top of the main Satellite Radio screen.
Favorites	Lets you manage artists and songs in the Favorites list and configure Alert Settings to let you know when favorite songs or artists are playing on other channels. Also, view a list of channels airing any of your Favorites.

ELECTRONICS

Browse Sub-Menu	Sub-Menu Description
Game Zone	Provides alerts when your favorite sports teams are starting a game which is being aired on other SiriusXM channels, or when their game score is announced. You can select and manage your Teams list here, and configure alerts.
Jump	Lets you select your favorite cities for Traffic & Weather information, which is used by the Jump feature on the main satellite radio screen.

Replay

• Lets you replay up to 44 minutes of the content of the current SiriusXM channel.

Replay Option	Option Description
Play/Pause	Touch to Pause content playback. Touch Pause/Play again to resume playback.
Rewind/RW	Rewinds the channel content in steps of 5 seconds. Touch and hold to rewind continuously, then release to begin playing content at that point.
Fast Forward/FW	Forwards the content, and works similarly to Rewind/RW. However, Fast Forward/FW can only be used when content has been previously rewound.
Replay Time	Displays the amount of time in the upper center of the screen by which your content lags the Live channel.
Live	Resumes playback of Live content at any time while replaying rewound content.

• SiriusXM services require subscriptions, sold separately after the 12-month trial included with the new vehicle purchase. **If you decide to continue your service at the end of your trial subscription, the plan you choose will automatically renew and bill at then-current rates until you call SiriusXM at 1-866-635-2349 for U.S. residents and 1-888-539-7474 for Canadian residents to cancel.** See SiriusXM Customer Agreement for complete terms at www.siriusxm.com. All fees and programming subject to change. Our satellite service is available only to those at least 18 and older in the 48 contiguous USA and D.C. Our Sirius satellite service is also available in PR (with coverage limitations). Our Internet radio service is available throughout our satellite service area and in AK and HI. Visit www.sirius.com/TravelLink for more information on SiriusXM Travel Link.© 2012 Sirius XM Radio Inc. Sirius, XM and all related marks and logos are trademarks of Sirius XM Radio Inc.

Disc Operation

• Your vehicle may have a remote CD player located in the lower center console storage bin, or in the lower center bench seat bin.

• CD/Disc Mode is entered by either inserting a CD/Disc or by touching the Media button located on the side of the display. Once in Media Mode, select Disc.

• Gently insert one CD into the CD player with the CD label facing as indicated on the illustration located on the Disc player.

Seek Up/Down Buttons

- Press to seek through Disc tracks.
- Hold either button to bypass tracks without stopping.

Browse

- Touch the browse soft-key to scroll through and select a desired track on the Disc. Touch the exit soft-key if you wish to cancel the browse function.

MEDIA HUB – PLAYING iPod/USB/MP3 DEVICES

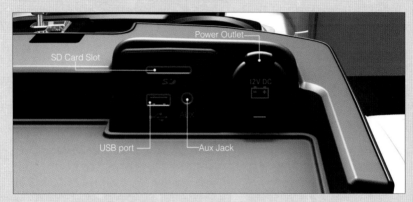

- There are many ways to play music from iPod®/MP3 players or USB devices through your vehicle's sound system.

Audio Jack (AUX)

- The AUX allows a portable device, such as an MP3 player or an iPod®, to be plugged into the radio and utilize the vehicle's sound system, using a 3.5 mm audio cable, to amplify the source and play through the vehicle speakers.
- Touching the Media soft-key then choosing AUX source will change the mode to auxiliary device if the audio jack is connected, allowing the music from your portable device to be heard through the vehicle's speakers. In order to activate the AUX, plug in the audio jack.
- The functions of the portable device are controlled using the device buttons. The volume may be controlled using the radio or portable device.
- To route the audio cable out of the center console, use the access cut out in the front of the console.

USB Port

- Connect your iPod® or compatible device using a USB cable into the USB Port. USB Memory sticks with audio files can also be used. Then, audio from the device can be played on the vehicles sound system while providing metadata (artist, track title, album, etc.) information on the radio display.

ELECTRONICS

- When connected, the iPod®/compatible USB device can be controlled using the radio or Steering Wheel Audio Controls to play, skip to the next or previous track, browse, and list the contents.

- The iPod® battery charges when plugged into the USB port (if supported by the specific device).

- To route the USB/iPod® cable out of the center console, use the access cut out.

NOTE:

- When connecting your iPod® device for the first time, the system may take several minutes to read your music, depending on the number of files. For example, the system will take approximately 5 minutes for every 1000 songs loaded on the device. Also during the reading process, the Shuffle and Browse functions will be disabled. This process is needed to ensure the full use of your iPod® features and only happens the first time it is connected. After the first time, the reading process of your iPod® will take considerably less time unless changes are made or new songs are added to the playlist.

- The USB port supports certain Mini, Classic, Nano, Touch, and iPhone® devices. The USB port also supports playing music from compatible external USB Mass Storage Class memory devices. Some iPod® software versions may not fully support the USB port features. Please visit Apple's website for iPod® software updates.

SD Card

- Play songs stored on an SD card inserted into the SD card slot.

- Song playback can be controlled using the radio or Steering Wheel Audio Controls to play, skip to the next or previous track, browse, and list the contents.

Bluetooth® Streaming Audio

- If equipped with Uconnect® Voice Command, your Bluetooth-equipped iPod® devices, cell phones or other media players, may also be able to stream music to your vehicle's sound system. Your connected device must be Bluetooth-compatible, and paired with your system (see Uconnect® Phone for pairing instructions). You can access the music from your connected Bluetooth® device by touching the Bluetooth® soft-key while in Media mode.

Uconnect® 8.4A & 8.4AN Available Media Hubs

Uconnect® 8.4A & 8.4AN	Media Hub (USB, AUX Ports)	Media Hub (SD, USB, AUX Ports)	Remote USB Port (Fully Functional)	Remote USB Port (Charging Only)	Dual Charging Ports
	-	S	S	O	O

S = Standard Equipment

O = Optional Equipment

iPod®/CD/AUX CONTROLS

- The iPod®/CD/AUX controls are accessed by touching the desired soft-key displayed on the side of the screen and choosing between Disc, AUX, iPod®, Bluetooth or SD Card.

NOTE:

Uconnect® Access will usually automatically switch to the appropriate mode when something is first connected or inserted into the system.

NAVIGATION

- Touch the Nav soft-key in the menu bar to access the Navigation system.

Changing the Navigation Voice Prompt Volume

1. Touch the View Map soft-key from the Nav Main Menu.
2. With the map displayed, touch the Settings soft-key in the lower right area of the screen.
3. In the Settings menu, touch the Guidance soft-key.
4. In the Guidance menu, adjust the Nav Volume by touching the + or – soft-keys.

ELECTRONICS

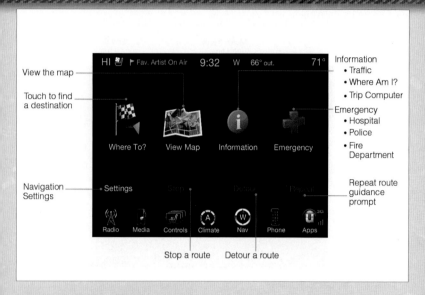

View the map

Touch to find a destination

Where To?   View Map   Information   Emergency

Information
• Traffic
• Where Am I?
• Trip Computer

Emergency
• Hospital
• Police
• Fire Department

Navigation Settings

Settings   Stop   Detour   Repeat

Radio   Media   Controls   Climate   Nav   Phone   Apps

Repeat route guidance prompt

Stop a route   Detour a route

Finding Points of Interest

- From the main Navigation menu, touch Where To? soft-key, then touch the Points of Interest soft-key.
- Select a Category and then a subcategory, if necessary.
- Select your destination and touch the Yes soft-key.

Finding a Place by Spelling the Name

- From the Main Navigation Menu, touch Where to? soft-key, then touch the Points of Interest soft-key and then touch the Spell Name soft-key.
- Enter the name of your destination.
- Touch the Done soft-key.
- Select your destination and touch the Yes soft-key.

Entering a Destination Address

- From the main Navigation menu, touch Where To? soft-key, then touch the Address soft-key.
- Follow the on-screen prompts to enter the address and touch the Yes soft-key.

NOTE:

Destination entry is not available while your vehicle is in motion. However, you can also use Voice Commands to enter an address while moving. Refer to Common Navigation Voice Commands in the Uconnect® Voice Command section.

Setting Your Home Location

- Touch the NAV soft-key in the menu bar to access the Navigation system and the Main Navigation menu.
- Touch Where To? soft-key, then touch the Go Home soft-key.
- You may enter your address directly, use your current location as your home address, or choose from recently found locations.
- To delete your Home location (or other saved locations) so you can save a new Home location, touch the Where To? soft-key from the Main Navigation menu, then touch the Go Home soft-key, and in the Yes screen touch the Options soft-key. In the Options menu touch the Clear Home soft-key. Set a new Home location by following the previous instructions.

Go Home

- A Home location must be saved in the system. From the Main Navigation menu, touch the Where To? soft-key, then touch the Go Home soft-key.

Next turn street – Touch to view Turn List

Distance to next turn

Estimated time of arrival – Touch to change data field

Zoom in and out

Your location on the map

Touch for Nav Main Me

Navigation Routing Options

Current street location

- Your route is marked with a blue line on the map. If you depart from the original route, your route is recalculated. A speed limit icon could appear as you travel on major roadways.

ELECTRONICS

Adding a Stop

- To add a stop you must be navigating a route.
- Touch the Menu soft-key to return to the Main Navigation menu.
- Touch Where To? soft-key, then search for the extra stop. When another location has been selected, you can choose to cancel your previous route, add as the first destination or add as the last destination.
- Touch the desired selection and touch the Yes soft-key.

Taking a Detour

- To take a detour you must be navigating a route.
- Touch the Detour soft-key.

NOTE:

- If the route you are currently taking is the only reasonable option, the device might not calculate a detour.
- For more information, see your Uconnect® Access User's Manual.

SiriusXM TRAFFIC (US Market Only)

Don't drive through traffic. Drive around it.

- Avoid congestion before you reach it. By enhancing your vehicle's navigation system with the ability to see detailed traffic information, you can pinpoint traffic incidents, determine average traffic speed and estimate travel time along your route. Since the service is integrated with a vehicle's navigation system, SiriusXM Traffic can help drivers pick the fastest route based on traffic conditions.

1. Detailed information on traffic speed, accidents, construction, and road closings.
2. Traffic information from multiple sources, including police and emergency services, cameras and road sensors.
3. Coast-to-coast delivery of traffic information.
4. View conditions for points along your route and beyond. Available in over 130 markets.

SiriusXM TRAVEL LINK (US Market Only)

- In addition to delivering over 130 channels of the best sports, entertainment, talk, and commercial-free music, SiriusXM offers premium data services that work in conjunction with compatible navigation systems. SiriusXM Travel Link brings a wealth of useful information into your vehicle and right to your fingertips.
- Weather -- Check variety of local and national weather information from radar maps to current and 5-day forecast.
- Fuel Prices -- Check local gas and diesel prices in your area and route to the station of your choice.
- Sports Scores -- In-game and final scores as well as weekly schedules.

- Movie Listings -- Check local movie theatres and listings in your area and route to the theater of your choice.

- SiriusXM Travel Link feature is completely integrated into your vehicle. A few minutes after you start your vehicle, Travel Link information arrives and updates in the background. You can access the information whenever you like, with no waiting.

- To access SiriusXM Travel Link, touch Apps soft-key, then the SiriusXM Travel Link soft-key.

NOTE:

- SiriusXM Travel Link requires a subscription, sold separately after the 1 year trial subscription included with your vehicle purchase.

- SiriusXM Travel Link is only available in the United States.

Fuel Prices	Check local gas and diesel prices in your area and route to the station of your choice.
Movie Listings	Check local movie theatres and listings in your area and route to the theater of your choice.
Sports Scores	In-game and final scores as well as weekly schedules.
Weather	Check variety of local and national weather information from radar maps to current and 5-day forecast.

Uconnect® Phone (Bluetooth® HANDS FREE CALLING)

- If the Uconnect® Phone Button 📞 exists on your steering wheel, then you have the Uconnect® Phone features.

- The Uconnect® Phone is a voice-activated, hands-free, in-vehicle communications system with Voice Command Capability (see Voice Command section).

- The Uconnect® Phone allows you to dial a phone number with your mobile phone using simple voice commands or using screen soft-keys.

- Refer to the Understand The Features Of Your Vehicle section of your vehicle's Owner's Manual on the DVD for further details.

NOTE:
The Uconnect® Phone requires a mobile phone equipped with the Bluetooth® Hands-Free Profile, Version 1.0 or higher. For Uconnect® Customer Support: U.S. residents visit www.UconnectPhone.com or call 1–877–855–8400. Canadian Residents call, 1-800-465–2001 (English) or 1-800-387-9983 (French).

Pairing a Phone

- To use the Uconnect® Phone feature, you must first pair your Bluetooth® phone with the Uconnect® system.

ELECTRONICS

Start pairing procedure on the radio

- Touch the Phone soft-key and then the Settings soft-key. Next, touch Add Device.
- Uconnect® Phone will display an "In progress" screen while the system is connecting.

Start pairing procedure on mobile phone

- Search for available devices on your Bluetooth® enabled mobile phone. This is usually within Settings or Options under "Bluetooth". See your mobile phone's manual for details.
- When your phone finds the system, select "Uconnect" as the paired device. You may be prompted by your phone to download the phonebook. This is so you can make calls by saying the name of your contact (PBAP-Phone Book Access Profile).

Complete the pairing procedure

- When prompted on the phone, enter the 4-digit PIN number shown on the Uconnect® Screen.
- If your phone asks you to accept a connection request from Uconnect, select "Yes". If available, check the box telling it not to ask again – that way your phone will automatically connect each time you start the vehicle.

Select the mobile phone's priority level

- When the pairing process has successfully completed, the system will prompt you to choose whether or not this is your favorite phone. Selecting Yes will make this phone the highest priority. This phone will take precedence over other paired phones within range. Only one phone can be paired at a time.
- You are now ready to make hands-free calls. Press the Uconnect® Phone button on your steering wheel to begin.

Making A Phone Call

- Press the Uconnect® Phone button ☎ .
- (After the BEEP), say "dial" then the number (or "call" then the name as listed in your phone; see Phonebook).

NOTE:
You can also initiate a call by using the touch-screen on the Phone main screen.

Receiving A Call – Accept (And End)

- When an incoming call rings/is announced on Uconnect®, press the Phone button ☎ .
- To end a call, press the Phone button ☎ .

Mute (Or Unmute) Microphone During Call

- During a call, touch the mute soft-key on the Phone main screen to mute and unmute the call.

ELECTRONICS

Transfer Ongoing Call Between Handset And Vehicle

- During a call, touch the Transfer soft-key on the Phone main screen to transfer an on-going call between handset and vehicle.

Common Phone Commands (Examples)

- "Call John Smith"
- "Call John Smith mobile"
- "Dial 1 248 555 1212"
- "Call Emergency"
- "Call Towing Assistance"
- "Redial"

Phonebook

- Uconnect® radios will automatically download your phonebook from your paired phone, if this feature is supported by your phone. Entries are updated each time that the phone is connected. If your phone book entries do not appear, check the settings on your phone. Some phones require you to enable this feature manually.
- Your phonebook can be browsed on your radio screen, but editing can only be done on your phone. To browse, touch the Phone soft-key, then the Phonebook soft-key.
- Favorite phonebook entries can be saved as Favorites for quicker access. Favorites are shown at the top of your main phone screen.

Voice Command Tips

- Using complete names (i.e; Call John Doe vs. Call John) will result in greater system accuracy.
- You can "chain" commands together for faster results. Say "Call John Doe, mobile", for example.
- If you are listening to available voice command options, you do not have to listen to the entire list. When you hear the command that you need, press the ((⸮ VR button on the steering wheel, wait for the beep and say your command.

Changing The Volume Of The Voice Command Prompts

- Start a dialogue by pressing the Phone button 📞 , then say a command, for example - "Help".
- Use the radio ON/OFF VOLUME rotary knob to adjust the Uconnect™ audio prompt volume to a comfortable level. Please note that the Uconnect™ audio prompt volume setting for Uconnect™ is different than the audio system.

NOTE:

To access help, press the Uconnect™ Phone 📞 button on the steering wheel and say "help." Touch the display or push either 📞 or ((⸮ VR button and say "cancel" to cancel the help session.

ELECTRONICS

Voice Texting

- Voice texting enhances the voice text reply feature built into your Uconnect 8.4A and Uconnect 8.4AN radio, and helps reduce driver distraction while keeping you connected. While voice text reply provides 18 pre-formatted messages you can send, voice texting lets you create and send nearly any message you want. Just speak your message as if you were talking to the recipient, and the Uconnect Access voice-to-text technology will convert your voice into a text message. Voice texting and voice text reply features are compatible with many newer Android and Blackberry phones. Before using, determine if your phone has been tested to support Bluetooth 'Message Access Protocol" (MAP) or AT Messaging Protocol at www.UconnectPhone.com, and ensure MAP is on and incoming message notification is enabled.

- Uconnect® Phone can read or send new text messages on your mobile phone.

- Your mobile phone must support SMS over Bluetooth® in order to use this feature. If the Uconnect® Phone determines your phone is not compatible with SMS messaging over Bluetooth® the "Messaging" button will be greyed out and the feature will not be available for use.

NOTE:

- For mobile phone compatibility and pairing instructions, please visit www.UconnectPhone.com

- Uconnect® Phone SMS touch-screen input is only available when the vehicle is not moving.

WARNING!

- Any voice commanded system should be used only in safe driving conditions following applicable laws regarding phone use. Your attention should be focused on safely operating the vehicle. Failure to do so may result in a collision causing you and others to be severely injured or killed.
- In an emergency, to use Uconnect® Phone, your mobile phone must be:
  - turned on,
  - paired to Uconnect® Phone,
  - and have network coverage.

VOICE COMMAND QUICK REFERENCE

Uconnect® 8.4AN Voice Command Quick Reference

- If the Uconnect® Voice Command «⧵ VR button exists on your steering wheel, you have the Voice Command feature, which is optimized for the driver. The Voice Command feature lets you keep your hands on the wheel, and your eyes on the road.

- When you press the Voice Command ⟪⟨ VR button located on the steering wheel, you will hear a beep. After the beep, give your command. If you do not know what commands to say, you can say "help" and the system will provide options to you. If you ever wish to interrupt the system while it lists options, press the Voice Command ⟪⟨ VR button, after the beep, say your command.

NOTE:
All phone oriented voice commands are accessible by first pressing the Phone Pick Up 📞 button, not the Voice Command button. To end a call, simply press the Phone Hang Up 📞 button. In some vehicles, the Phone Pickup 📞 button serves the dual purpose of ending calls as well.

Voice Command (VR) User TIPs

- To hear available commands, press the Uconnect® Voice Command button and say "Help". You will hear available commands for the menu displayed.

- At any time, you can say the words "Cancel" or "Help". These commands are universal and can be used from virtually any menu. All other specific commands can be used depending upon the active application.

- You can interrupt the system prompts at any time by pressing the Uconnect® Voice Command button while the system is speaking. After the beep, you can say a command.

- You can 'chain' commands together for faster results. Say "Call Joe Doe mobile", for example.

- For best performance, adjust the rearview mirror to provide at least 1/2 in (1 cm) gap between the overhead console (if equipped) and the mirror.

- Always wait for the beep before speaking.

- Speak normally, without pausing, just as you would speak to a person sitting a few feet/meters away from you.

- Make sure that no one other than you is speaking during a Voice Command period.

Steering Wheel Buttons

- You can control many of your radio features using your voice. Press either the VR ⟪⟨ VR or Phone Pick Up 📞 button on your steering wheel.

Available Radio Soft–Key Voice Commands

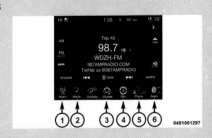

Steering Wheel Buttons to Press:	(1) Radio Mode	(2) Media Mode	(3) Climate Controls	(4) Navigation	(5) Phone Mode	(6) APPS
Uconnect® Voice Command (VR) Button	AM/FM & Satellite Brand Control	Media Devices Control	Temperature Control	Destination Selection and View		BING
Types of Voice Commands Available			GENERAL			
Uconnect® Phone Pick Up Button	-	-	-	-	Call Initiation, Call Management, Pre-formatted Voice Text Reply	-

ELECTRONICS

Voice Command Examples – Uconnect® 8.4AN

GENERAL	
Anytime	"Go to Radio" (Media, Climate, Navigation, Phone, Apps) – Settings, and Controls are not Voice Command accessible "Cancel" "Help" (to listen to suggested commands specific to current need "Repeat" "Launch BING" – Required 1st voice command to launch BING app "BING Search" – Required 2nd voice command to activate app functionality using Steering Wheel Voice Control Button
RADIO	
AM/FM	"Tune to AM950", "Tune to 95.5FM (preset 5)"
Satellite Band Control	"Tune to Satellite Channel 80's on 8", Tune to Satellite Channel 32 (preset 4)
MEDIA	
Media Devices Control (Functionality is dependent on compatibility between devises and radio)	"Browse" (show) "artist" (albums, music) "Show paired phones" (devices) "Play song – Maple Leaf Rag" (artist - Scott Joplin, genre - rock, album - Ragtime Favorites) "Shuffle" – available with iPod, USB and SD Card
CLIMATE	
Temperature Control	"Set temperature to 70 degrees" – single climate zone vehicles
	"Set driver" (passenger) "temperature to 75 degrees" – dual climate zone vehicles
NAVIGATION	
Destination Selection & View	"Enter address" (provide location inputs sequentially, via audible radio prompts) "Go Home" – destination previously defined by driver "Repeat guidance" – hear the last navigation prompt "Cancel Route" "View Map"
PHONE	
Call Initiation (Requires that phone has been Bluetooth® paired with radio	"Dial 123-456-7890" (phone number) "Call John Smith mobile" (home, office, other) "Redial" "Show outgoing" (recent) "calls"
Call Management	"Search for John Smith" (any contact name in address book) "Show (display list) contacts"

ELECTRONICS

Voice Texting (Available during trial period or if subscribed to Uconnect® Access Advantage)	Create a text message using Voice Command Capability "Send a message to John Smith (123-456-7890)" "Show Messages" "Listen to" (view) "number 4" "Forward text" (message) "to John Smith" (phone type, number)
Voice Text Reply (Radio audibly recognizes these 18 pre-formatted SMS messages as you speak)	Forward one of 18 pre-formatted SMS messages to incoming calls/text messages: "Yes." "No." "Okay." "I can't talk right now." "Call me." "I'll call you later." "I'm on my way." "Thanks." "I'll be late." "I will be <number> minutes late." "See you in <number> minutes" "Stuck in traffic." "Start without me." "Where are you?" "Are you there yet?" "I need directions." "I'm lost." "See you later."
APPS	
SiriusXM Travel Link (Traffic function is not voice command accessible within SiriusXM Travel Link	"Show Fuel prices" "Show Current Weather" – provides access to Forecast as well "Show Weather map" – multiple map formats available "Show Sports" "Show Movie listings" "Show My favorites"
BING (BING adds it's own audible prompts, and response time varies depending on carrier coverage speed)	"Launch BING" – Required 1st voice command to launch BING app "BING Search" – Required 2nd voice command to activate app functionality using Steering Wheel Voice Control Button "Hotel" (restaurant, gas station, mail, hospital) – for nearest desired general POI "Italian restaurants" – for nearest specified POI category "Hotels" (restaurants, hospitals, Starbucks) "in Miami" (location) – specified distance POI

STEERING WHEEL AUDIO CONTROLS

- The steering wheel audio controls are located on the rear surface of the steering wheel.

Right Switch

- Press the switch up or down to increase or decrease the volume.

- Press the button in the center to change modes AM/FM/CD/SXM.

Left Switch

- Press the switch up or down to search for the next listenable station or select the next or previous CD track.

Steering Wheel Audio Controls

- Press the button in the center to select the next preset station (radio) or to change CDs if equipped with a CD Changer.

ELECTRONIC VEHICLE INFORMATION CENTER (EVIC)

EVIC Controls

- The EVIC features a driver interactive display that is located in the instrument cluster. Pressing the controls on the left side of the steering wheel allows the driver to select vehicle information and Personal Settings. For additional information, refer to Programmable Features in this guide.

- Press and release the UP △ button to scroll upward through the main menus (Fuel Economy, Vehicle Info, Tire PSI, Cruise, Messages, Trip Info, Vehicle Speed and Turn Menu Off) and sub menus.

- Press and release the DOWN ▽ button to scroll downward through the main menus and sub menus.

- Press and release the RIGHT ▷ button for access to main menus, sub menus or to select a personal setting in the setup menu. Press and hold the RIGHT ▷ button for two seconds to reset features

- Press the BACK/LEFT ◁ button to scroll back to a previous menu or sub menu.

ELECTRONICS

Compass Calibration

• This compass is self-calibrating, which eliminates the need to set the compass manually. When the vehicle is new, the compass may appear erratic and the EVIC will display "CAL" until the compass is calibrated.

• You may also calibrate the compass by completing one or more 360 degree turns (in an area free from large metal or metallic objects) until the "CAL" message displayed in the EVIC turns off. The compass will now function normally.

PROGRAMMABLE FEATURES

Programmable Features

• The EVIC can be used to view or change the following settings. Press the UP △ or DOWN ▽ button until System Setup displays, then press the RIGHT ▷ button. Scroll through the settings using the UP or DOWN buttons. Press the RIGHT ▷ button to change the setting. Press the BACK/LEFT ◁ button to scroll back to a previous menu or sub menu.

  • Radio Info
  • Fuel Economy Info
  • Cruise Control Info
  • Digital Vehicle Speed
  • Stop/Start
  • Screen Setup

  • Trip Info
  • Tire Pressure
  • Vehicle Info
  • Stored Warning Messages
  • Turn Menu OFF

Uconnect® Access Customer Programmable Features

• The Uconnect® Access system allows you to access Customer Programmable feature settings such as Display, Clock, Safety/Assistance, Lights, Doors & Locks, Heated Seats, Engine Off Operation, Compass Settings, Audio, Phone/ Bluetooth and SiriusXM Setup through soft-keys.

• Touch the More soft-key to on the bottom of the screen, then touch the Settings soft-key to access the Settings screen. When making a selection, scroll up or down until the preferred setting is highlighted, then press and release the preferred setting until a check-mark appears next to the setting, showing that setting has been selected. The following feature settings are available:

  • Display
  • Safety / Assistance
  • Auto-On Comfort & Remote Start
  • Compass
  • Phone / Bluetooth
  • Lights

  • Clock
  • Doors & Locks
  • Engine Off Options
  • Audio
  • SiriusXM Setup

EVIC Reconfigurable Screen Setup

- The following settings allow you to change what information is displayed in the instrument cluster as well as the location that information is displayed.

Digital Speedometer

- Press and release the UP or DOWN arrow button until the Digital display icon is highlighted in the EVIC. Press and release the RIGHT arrow button to change the display between km/h and mph.

Vehicle Info (Customer Information Features)

- Press and release the UP or DOWN button until the Vehicle Info icon is highlighted in the EVIC. Press and release the RIGHT button and Coolant Temp will be displayed. Press the UP or DOWN arrow button to scroll through the following information sub-menus:
- Tire Pressure
- Coolant Temperature

Trip A

- Press and release the UP or DOWN arrow button until the Trip A icon is highlighted in the EVIC. Press and release the RIGHT arrow button to display the Trip A information.

Trip B

- Press and release the UP or DOWN arrow button until the Trip B icon is highlighted in the EVIC. Press and release the RIGHT arrow button to display the Trip B information.

Fuel Economy

- Press and release the UP or DOWN arrow button until the Fuel Economy icon is highlighted. Press the RIGHT arrow button and the next screen will display the following:
  - Average Fuel Economy/Miles Per Gallon (MPG Bargraph)
  - Range To Empty (RTE)
  - Current Miles Per Gallon (MPG)

Stop/Start

- Press and release the UP or DOWN arrow button until the Stop/Start icon is highlighted in the EVIC. Press and release the RIGHT arrow button to display the Stop/Start status.

ELECTRONICS

Trailer Tow

• Press and release the UP or DOWN arrow button until the Trailer Tow icon is highlighted. Press the RIGHT arrow button and the next screen will display the following trailer trip information:
  • Trailer Trip
  • Trailer Brake
  • Multimeter

Audio

• Press and release the UP or DOWN arrow button until the Audio display icon is highlighted in the EVIC. Press and release the RIGHT arrow button to display the active source and the audio information.

Screen Setup

• Press and release the UP or DOWN arrow button until the Screen Setup display icon is highlighted in the EVIC. Press and release the RIGHT arrow button to enter the Screen Setup sub-menu. The Screen Setup feature allows you to change what information is displayed in the instrument cluster as well as the location that information is displayed.

UNIVERSAL GARAGE DOOR OPENER (HomeLink®)

• HomeLink® replaces up to three hand-held transmitters that operate devices such as garage door openers, motorized gates, lighting or home security systems. The HomeLink® unit is powered by your vehicles 12 Volt battery.

• The HomeLink® buttons that are located in the overhead console or sunvisor designate the three different HomeLink® channels.

• The HomeLink® indicator is located above the center button.

Before You Begin Programming HomeLink®

HomeLink® Buttons

• Be sure that your vehicle is parked outside of the garage before you begin programming.

• For more efficient programming and accurate transmission of the radio-frequency signal it is recommended that a new battery be placed in the hand-held transmitter of the device that is being programmed to the HomeLink® system.

• Erase all channels before you begin programming. To erase the channels, place the ignition switch into the ON/RUN position, then press and hold the two outside HomeLink® buttons (I and III) for up 20 seconds or until the red indicator flashes.

NOTE:

- Erasing all channels should only be performed when programming HomeLink® for the first time. Do not erase channels when programming additional buttons.

- If you have any problems, or require assistance, please call toll-free 1–800–355–3515 or, on the Internet at www.HomeLink.com for information or assistance.

Programming A Rolling Code

- For programming Garage Door Openers that were manufactured after 1995. These Garage Door Openers can be identified by the "LEARN" or "TRAIN" button located where the hanging antenna is attached to the Garage Door Opener. It is NOT the button that is normally used to open and close the door. The name and color of the button may vary by manufacturer.

1. Place the ignition switch into the ON/RUN position.

2. Place the hand-held transmitter 1 to 3 in (3 to 8 cm) away from the HomeLink® button you wish to program while keeping the HomeLink® indicator light in view.

3. Simultaneously press and hold both the Homelink® button you want to program and the hand-held transmitter button.

4. Continue to hold buttons until the EVIC display changes from "CHANNEL # TRAINING" to "CHANNEL # TRAINED", then release both buttons.

NOTE:
If the EVIC displays "DID NOT TRAIN" repeat from Step 2.

5. At the garage door opener motor (in the garage), locate the "LEARN" or "TRAINING" button. This can usually be found where the hanging antenna wire is attached to the garage door opener motor. Firmly press and release the "LEARN" or "TRAINING" button.

NOTE:
You have 30 seconds in which to initiate the next step after the LEARN button has been pressed.

6. Return to the vehicle and press the programmed HomeLink® button twice (holding the button for two seconds each time). The EVIC will display "CHANNEL # TRANSMIT". If the garage door opener/device activates, programming is complete.

NOTE:
If the device does not activate, press the button a third time (for two seconds) to complete the training.

7. To program the remaining two HomeLink® buttons, repeat each step for each remaining button. DO NOT erase the channels.

ELECTRONICS

Programming A Non-Rolling Code

• For programming Garage Door Openers manufactured before 1995.

1. Turn the ignition switch to the ON/RUN position.

2. Place the hand-held transmitter 1 to 3 in (3 to 8 cm) away from the HomeLink® button you wish to program while keeping the HomeLink® indicator light in view.

3. Simultaneously press and hold both the HomeLink® button you want to program and the hand-held transmitter button.

4. Continue to hold buttons until the EVIC display changes from "CHANNEL # TRAINING" to "CHANNEL # TRAINED", then release both buttons.

5. Press and hold the programmed HomeLink® button and observe the indicator light.

NOTE:

• If the EVIC displays "DID NOT TRAIN" repeat from Step 2.

• To program the two remaining HomeLink® buttons, repeat each step for each remaining button. DO NOT erase the channels.

Using HomeLink®

• To operate, press and release the programmed HomeLink® button. Activation will now occur for the programmed device (i.e., garage door opener, gate operator, security system, entry door lock, home/office lighting, etc.,). The hand-held transmitter of the device may also be used at any time.

WARNING!
• Your motorized door or gate will open and close while you are programming the universal transceiver. Do not program the transceiver if people or pets are in the path of the door or gate.
• Do not run your vehicle in a closed garage or confined area while programming the transceiver. Exhaust gas from your vehicle contains Carbon Monoxide (CO) which is odorless and colorless. Carbon Monoxide is poisonous when inhaled and can cause you and others to be severely injured or killed.

ELECTRONICS

POWER INVERTER

- A 115 Volt, 150 Watt power inverter outlet is located on the lower instrument panel next to the climate control knob. This outlet can power cellular phones, electronics and other low power devices requiring power up to 150 Watts.

- To turn on the power outlet, simply plug in the device. The outlet automatically turns off when the device is unplugged.

NOTE:

The power inverter is designed with built-in overload protection. If the power rating of 150 Watts is exceeded, the

Power Inverter Outlet

power inverter will automatically shut down. Once the electrical device has been removed from the outlet, the inverter should automatically reset.

WARNING!

To Avoid Serious Injury or Death DO NOT:
- insert any objects into the receptacles
- touch with wet hands

Close the lid when not in use. If this outlet is mishandled, it may cause an electric shock and failure.

ELECTRONICS

POWER OUTLETS

- The auxiliary 12 Volt (13 Amp) power outlets can provide power for in-cab accessories designed for use with the standard "cigar lighter" plug. The 12 Volt power outlets have a cap attached to the outlet indicating "12V DC", together with either a key symbol or a battery symbol.

- The auxiliary power outlets can be found in the following locations:
  - Lower left and lower right in the center of the instrument panel – if equipped with a column or a eight-speed electronic shifter.
  - Inside the top storage tray.
  - Inside the upper lid of the center storage compartment — if equipped.
  - Rear of the center console storage compartment — Quad Cab® or Crew Cab.

Power Outlet

NOTE:

- Do not exceed the maximum power of 160 Watts (13 Amps) at 12 Volts. If the 160 Watt (13 Amp) power rating is exceeded, the fuse protecting the system will need to be replaced.

- Power outlets are designed for accessory plugs only. Do not insert any other object in the power outlet as this will damage the outlet and blow the fuse. Improper use of the power outlet can cause damage not covered by your new vehicle warranty.

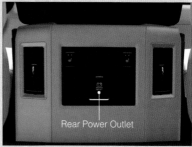

Rear Power Outlet

FOUR WHEEL DRIVE OPERATION

FOUR-POSITION/PART TIME TRANSFER CASE

- The transfer case provides four mode positions:
    - Two-wheel drive high range (2WD)
    - Four-wheel drive high range (4WD LOCK)
    - NEUTRAL (N)
    - Four-wheel drive low range (4WD LOW)

- This transfer case is intended to be driven in the 2WD position for normal street and highway conditions, such as dry, hard-surfaced roads.

- When additional traction is required, the 4WD LOCK and 4WD LOW positions can be used to lock the front and rear driveshafts together.

- When operating your vehicle in 4WD LOW, do not exceed 25 mph (40 km/h).

Shifting Procedure

- Shifting between 2WD and 4WD LOCK can be made with the vehicle stopped or in motion at speeds up to 55 mph (88 km/h).

- Shifting between 2WD or 4WD LOCK into 4WD LOW must be made with the transmission in NEUTRAL and the vehicle stopped or rolling at 2 to 3 mph (3 to 5 km/h).

FIVE-POSITION/ON-DEMAND TRANSFER CASE

- This electronically shifted transfer case provides five mode positions:
    - Two-wheel drive high range (2WD)
    - Four-wheel drive automatic range (4WD AUTO)
    - Four-wheel drive lock range (4WD LOCK)
    - Four-wheel drive low range (4WD LOW)
    - NEUTRAL (N)

OFF-ROAD CAPABILITIES

- This electronically shifted transfer case is designed to be driven in the two-wheel drive position (2WD) or four-wheel drive position (4WD AUTO) for normal street and highway conditions on dry, hard-surfaced roads.

- Driving the vehicle in 2WD will have greater fuel economy benefits as the front axle is not engaged in 2WD.

Shifting Procedure

- Shifting between 2WD and 4WD AUTO or 4WD LOCK can be made with the vehicle stopped or in motion at speeds up to 55 mph (88 km/h).

- Shifting between 2WD, 4WD AUTO and 4WD LOCK into 4WD LOW must be made with the transmission in NEUTRAL and the vehicle stopped or rolling at 2 to 3 mph (3 to 5 km/h).

NOTE:
It is preferred to have the engine running and the vehicle moving at 2 to 3 mph (3 to 5 km/h).

WARNING!

You or others could be injured if you leave the vehicle unattended with the transfer case in the NEUTRAL position without first fully engaging the parking brake. The transfer case NEUTRAL position disengages both the front and rear driveshafts from the powertrain and will allow the vehicle to move regardless of the transmission position. The parking brake should always be applied when the driver is not in the vehicle.

FIVE-POSITION/ON-DEMAND TRANSFER CASE

- This electronically shifted transfer case provides five mode positions:
  - Two-wheel drive high range (2WD)
  - Four-wheel drive automatic range (4WD AUTO)
  - Four-wheel drive lock range (4WD LOCK)
  - Four-wheel drive low range (4WD LOW)
  - NEUTRAL (N)

4WD Switch (8 Speed Transmission Only)

- This electronically shifted transfer case is designed to be driven in the two-wheel drive position (2WD) or four-wheel drive position (4WD AUTO) for normal street and highway conditions on dry, hard-surfaced roads.

- Driving the vehicle in 2WD will have greater fuel economy benefits as the front axle is not engaged in 2WD.

Shifting Procedure

- Shifting between 2WD and 4WD AUTO or 4WD LOCK can be made with the vehicle stopped or in motion at speeds up to 55 mph (88 km/h).
- Shifting between 2WD, 4WD AUTO and 4WD LOCK into 4WD LOW must be made with the transmission in NEUTRAL and the vehicle stopped or rolling at 2 to 3 mph (3 to 5 km/h).

NOTE:

It is preferred to have the engine running and the vehicle moving at 2 to 3 mph (3 to 5 km/h).

WARNING!

You or others could be injured if you leave the vehicle unattended with the transfer case in the NEUTRAL position without first fully engaging the parking brake. The transfer case NEUTRAL position disengages both the front and rear driveshafts from the powertrain and will allow the vehicle to move regardless of the transmission position. The parking brake should always be applied when the driver is not in the vehicle.

UTILITY

TONNEAU COVER

- The Tonneau Cover can be removed and reinstalled by using the locking clamps located underneath the Tonneau Cover.

NOTE:
Be sure that the Tonneau Cover is secured before driving.

EASY-OFF TAILGATE

- To simplify mounting of a camper unit with an overhang, the tailgate can be removed.

NOTE:
If your vehicle is equipped with a rear camera or RKE the electrical connector must be disconnected prior to removing the tailgate.

Removing the Tailgate

- Disconnect the wiring harness for the rear camera or RKE (if equipped).
- Unlatch the tailgate and remove the support cables by releasing the lock tang from the pivot.
- Raise the right side of the tailgate until the right side pivot clears the hanger bracket.
- Slide the entire tailgate to the right to free the left side pivot.
- Remove the tailgate from the vehicle.

NOTE:
Do not carry the tailgate loose in the truck pickup box.

Locking Tailgate

- The lock is located next to the tailgate handle. The tailgate can be locked using the vehicle key.

WARNING!

To avoid inhaling carbon monoxide, which is deadly, the exhaust system on vehicles equipped with "Cap or Slide-In Campers" should extend beyond the overhanging camper compartment and be free of leaks.

PICKUP BOX

- You can carry wide building materials (sheets of plywood, etc.) by building a raised load floor. Place lumber across the box in the indentations provided above the wheel housings and in the bulkhead dividers to form the floor.

- There are stampings in the sheet metal on the inner side bulkheads of the box in front of and behind both wheel housings. Place wooden boards across the box from side to side to create separate load compartments in the pickup box.

- There are four tie-down cleats bolted to the lower sides of the pickup box that can sustain loads up to 1000 lbs (450 kg) total.

NOTE:
If you are installing a Toolbox, Ladder Rack or Headache Rack at the front of the Pickup Box, you must use Mopar Box Reinforcement Brackets that are available from your authorized dealer.

WARNING!

- The pickup box is intended for load carrying purposes only, not for passengers, who should sit in seats and use seat belts.
- Care should always be exercised when operating a vehicle with unrestrained cargo. Vehicle speeds may need to be reduced. Severe turns or rough roads may cause shifting or bouncing of the cargo that may result in vehicle damage. If wide building materials are to be frequently carried, the installation of a support is recommended. This will restrain the cargo and transfer the load to the pickup box floor.
- If you wish to carry more than 600 lbs (272 kg) of material suspended above the wheelhouse, supports must be installed to transfer the weight of the load to the pickup box floor or vehicle damage may result. The use of proper supports will permit loading up to the rated payload.
- Unrestrained cargo may be thrown forward in an accident causing serious or fatal injury.

UTILITY

RAMBOX®

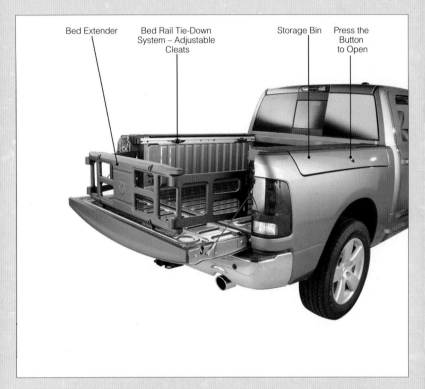

Bed Extender — Bed Rail Tie-Down System – Adjustable Cleats — Storage Bin — Press the Button to Open

- The RamBox® system is an integrated pickup box storage and cargo management system consisting of three features:
  - Integrated box side storage bins
  - Cargo extender/divider
  - Bed rail tie-down system

NOTE:
If you are installing a Toolbox, Ladder Rack or Headache Rack at the front of the Pickup Box, you must use Mopar Box Reinforcement Brackets that are available from your authorized dealer.

RamBox® Integrated Box Side Storage Bins

- The cargo storage bins provide watertight, lockable, illuminated storage for up to 150 lbs (68 kg) of evenly distributed cargo.

- To open a storage bin, press and release the pushbutton located on the lid.

- The interior of the RamBox® will automatically illuminate when the lid is opened. Pushing the switch once will turn off the bin lights, pushing the switch again will turn the lights back on.

- Storage bins feature two removable drain plugs (to allow water to drain from bins). To remove plug, pull up on the edge. To install, push plug downward into drain hole.

- The RamBox® storage bins can be locked and unlocked using the vehicle key or the remote keyless entry transmitter.

NOTE:
Provisions are provided in the bins for cargo dividers and shelf supports. These accessories (in addition to other RamBox® accessories) are available from MOPAR®.

RamBox® Storage Bin Cover Emergency Release Lever

- As a security measure, a Storage Bin Cover Emergency Release is built into the storage bin cover latching mechanism.

NOTE:
In the event of an individual being locked inside the storage bin, the storage bin cover can be opened from inside of the bin by pulling on the glow-in-the-dark lever attached to the storage bin cover latching mechanism.

Bed Extender

- The bed extender has three functional positions:
  - Storage Position
  - Divider Position
  - Extender Position

Storage Position

- The storage position for the bed extender is at the front of the truck bed.

- To install the bed extender into the storage position, perform the following:
  - Make sure the center handle is unlocked using the vehicle key and rotate the center handle vertically to release the extender side gates.
  - With the side gates open, position the extender fully forward in the bed against the front panel.
  - Rotate the side gates closed allowing the outboard ends to be positioned in front of the cargo tie-down loops.
  - Rotate the center handle horizontally to secure the side gates in the closed position.
  - Lock the center handle using the vehicle key to secure the panel into place and assist against theft.

UTILITY

Divider Position

- There are 11 divider slots along the bed inner panels which allow for various positions to assist in managing your cargo.
- To install the bed extender into a divider position perform the following:
  - Make sure the center handle is unlocked using the vehicle key and rotate the center handle vertically to release the extender side gates.
  - With the side gates open, position the extender so the outboard ends align with the intended slots in the sides of the bed.
  - Rotate the side gates closed so that the outboard ends are secured into the intended slots of the bed.
  - Rotate the center handle horizontally to secure the side gates in the closed position.
  - Lock the center handle to secure the panel into place and assist against theft.

Extender Position

- The bed extender will add an additional 15 in (38 cm) in the back of the truck when additional cargo room is needed.
- To install the bed extender into the extender position, perform the following:
  - Lower the tailgate.
  - Make sure the center handle is unlocked and rotate the center handle vertically in order to release the extender side gates.
  - Fit the end of the side gate ends onto the pin and handle.
  - Rotate the handles to the horizontal position to secure into place.

Bed Rail Tie-Down System

- There are two adjustable cleats on each side of the bed that can be used to assist in securing cargo.
- Each cleat must be located and tightened down in one of the detents, along either rail, in order to keep cargo properly secure.
- To move the cleat to any position on the rail, turn the nut counterclockwise, approximately three turns. Then, pull out on the cleat and slide it to the detent nearest the desired location. Make sure the cleat is seated in the detent and tighten the nut.
- To remove the cleats from the utility rail, remove the end cap by pushing up on the locking tab, located on the bottom of the end cap. Slide the cleat off the end of the rail.

CAUTION!

- Failure to follow the following items could cause damage to the vehicle:
  - Assure that all cargo inside the storage bins is properly secured.
  - Do not exceed cargo weight rating of 150 lb (68 kg) per bin.
  - Leaving the lid open for extended periods of time could cause the vehicle battery to discharge. If the lid is required to stay open for extended periods of time, it is recommended that the bin lights be turned off manually using the on/off switch.
  - Ensure cargo bin lids are closed and latched before moving or driving vehicle.
  - Loads applied to the top of the bin lid should be minimized to prevent damage to the lid and latching/hinging mechanisms.
  - Damage to the RamBox® bin may occur due to heavy/sharp objects placed in bin that shift due to vehicle motion. In order to minimize potential for damage, secure all cargo to prevent movement and protect inside surfaces of bin from heavy/sharp objects with appropriate padding.
  - The maximum load per cleat should not exceed 250 lbs (113 kg) and the angle of the load on each cleat should not exceed 60 degrees above horizontal, or damage to the cleat or cleat rail may occur.

WARNING!

- Always close the storage bin covers when your vehicle is unattended or in motion.
- Do not allow children to have access to the storage bins. Once in the storage bin, young children may not be able to escape. If trapped in the storage bin, children can die from suffocation or heat stroke.
- In a collision, serious injury could result if the storage bin covers are not properly latched.
- Do not use a storage bin latch as a tie down.
- To reduce the risk of potential injury or property damage:
  - Cargo must be secured.
  - Do not exceed cargo load rating of your vehicle.
  - Secure all loads to truck utilizing cargo tie-downs.
  - Extender should not be used as cargo tie-down.
  - When vehicle is in motion do not exceed 150 lbs (68 kg) load on the tailgate.
  - The bed extender is not intended for off road use.
  - When not in use, the extender/divider should be in stowed or divider position with the tailgate closed.
  - When in use, all handles are to be in the locked position.

UTILITY

TOWING & PAYLOAD

Ram 1500 4x2

	ST	SLT/Outdoorsman	Sport/Laramie
3.6L V-6 8–Speed Automatic Transmission	Standard Towing: 5,000 lbs (2 268 kg) Max Towing: 6,500 lbs (2 948 kg) Max Payload: 1,910 lbs (866 kg)	Standard Towing: 5,000 lbs (2 268 kg) Max Towing: 6,500 lbs (2 948 kg) Max Payload: 1,890 lbs (857 kg)	—
4.7L V-8 6–Speed Automatic Transmission	Standard Towing: 5,000 lbs (2 268 kg) Max Towing: 7,700 lbs (3 492 kg) Max Payload: 1,750 lbs (793 kg)	Standard Towing: 5,000 lbs (2 268 kg) Max Towing: 7,700 lbs (3 492 kg) Max Payload: 1,720 lbs (780 kg)	—
5.7L HEMI®V-8 6–Speed Automatic Transmission	Standard Towing: 5,000 lbs (2 268 kg) Max Towing: 10,450 lbs (4 740 kg) Max Payload: 1,710 lbs (775 kg)	Standard Towing: 5,000 lbs (2 268 kg) Max Towing: 10,450 lbs (4 740 kg) Max Payload: 1,690 lbs (766 kg)	Standard Towing: 5,000 lbs (2 268 kg) Max Towing: 10,300 lbs (4 672 kg) Max Payload: 1,550 lbs (703 kg)

Ram 1500 4x4

	ST	SLT/Outdoorsman	Sport/Laramie
3.6L V-6 8–Speed Automatic Transmission	Standard Towing: 5,000 lbs (2 268 kg) Max Towing: 6,300 lbs (2 857 kg) Max Payload: 1,930 lbs (875 kg)	Standard Towing: 5,000 lbs (2 268 kg) Max Towing: 6,250 lbs (2 834 kg) Max Payload: 1,900 lbs (861 kg)	—
4.7L V-8 6–Speed Automatic Transmission	Standard Towing: 5,000 lbs (2 268 kg) Max Towing: 7,500 lbs (3 401 kg) Max Payload: 1,570 lbs (712 kg)	Standard Towing: 5,000 lbs (2 268 kg) Max Towing: 7,450 lbs (3 379 kg) Max Payload: 1,530 lbs (694 kg)	—

	ST	SLT/Outdoorsman	Sport/Laramie
5.7L HEMI®V-8 6–Speed Automatic Transmission	Standard Towing: 5,000 lbs (2 268 kg) Max Towing: 10,350 lbs (4 694 kg) Max Payload: 1,480 lbs (671 kg)	Standard Towing: 5,000 lbs (2 268 kg) Max Towing: 10,300 lbs (4 672 kg) Max Payload: 1,450 lbs (657 kg)	Standard Towing: 5,000 lbs (2 268 kg) Max Towing: 10,050 lbs (4 558 kg) Max Payload: 1,380 lbs (625 kg)

Ram 2500 & 3500

	ST	SLT/OUTDOORSMAN/	SPORT/LARAMIE
5.7L HEMI® V-8 6-Speed Automatic Transmission	Max Towing: 10,100 lbs (4 581 kg) Max Payload: 1,780 lbs (807 kg)	Max Towing: 12,300 lbs (5 579 kg) Max Payload: 3,120 lbs (1 415 kg)	—

Diesel

	2500 ST SLT Bighorn/ Lonestar Laramie Outdoorsman	3500 ST SLT Bighorn/ Lonestar Laramie Outdoorsman
6.7L Cummins® Turbo Diesel 6-Speed Manual Transmission	Max Towing: 16,900 lbs (7 665 kg) Max Payload: 2,960 lbs (1 342 kg)	Max Towing: 18,200 lbs (8 255 kg) Max Payload: 6,640 lbs (3 011 kg)
6.7L Cummins® Turbo Diesel 6-Speed Automatic Transmission	Max Towing: 17,870 lbs (8 105 kg) Max Payload: 3,020 lbs (1 369 kg)	Max Towing: 30,060 lbs (13 634 kg) Max Payload: 6,710 lbs (3 043 kg)

NOTE:

For additional trailer towing information (maximum trailer weight ratings) refer to the following website addresses:

• **http://www.ramtrucks.com**.

• **http://www.ramtruck.ca** (Canada).

UTILITY

TOW/HAUL MODE

- When driving in hilly areas, towing a trailer, carrying a heavy load, etc., and frequent transmission shifting occurs, press the TOW/HAUL switch to select TOW/HAUL mode. This will improve performance and reduce the potential for transmission overheating or failure due to excessive shifting. When operating in TOW/HAUL mode, transmission upshifts are delayed, and the transmission will automatically downshift (for engine braking) during steady braking maneuvers.

- The "TOW/HAUL Indicator Light" will illuminate in the instrument cluster to indicate that TOW/HAUL mode has been activated. Pressing the switch a second time restores normal operation. If the TOW/HAUL mode is desired, the switch must be pressed each time the engine is started.

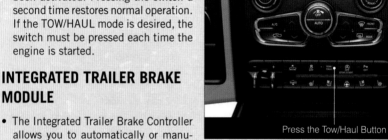

Press the Tow/Haul Button

INTEGRATED TRAILER BRAKE MODULE

- The Integrated Trailer Brake Controller allows you to automatically or manually activate the Electric Trailer Brakes and Electric Over Hydraulic Trailer Brakes for a better braking performance when towing a trailer.

NOTE:
The Integrated Trailer Brake Controller is located in the center stack below the climate controls.

- This module will have four different options depending on the type of trailer you want to tow and can be selected through the Electronic Vehicle Information Center (EVIC) or touch-screen radio – if equipped.
  - Light Electric
  - Heavy Electric
  - Light EOH (Electric Over Hydraulic)
  - Heavy EOH (Electric Over Hydraulic)

- To make the proper selection in the Electronic Vehicle Information Center (EVIC), press the UP or DOWN steering wheel buttons until "VEHICLE SETTINGS" displays. For additional information, refer to Electronics in this guide.

- Press the RIGHT arrow on the steering wheel to enter "VEHICLE SETTINGS."

- Press the UP or DOWN buttons until Trailer Brake Type appears on the screen.

- Press the RIGHT arrow and then press the UP or DOWN buttons until the proper Trailer Brake Type appears on the screen.

GAIN Adjustment Buttons (+/-)

- Pressing the +/- buttons, located on the left side of the module, will increase/decrease the brake control power output to the trailer brakes in 0.5 increments. The GAIN setting can be increased to a maximum of 10 or decreased to a minimum of 0 (no trailer braking).

- Refer to your Owner's Manual on the DVD for further details.

GAIN Adjustment Buttons

WARNING!
Connecting a trailer that is not compatible with the ITBM system may result in reduced or complete loss of trailer braking. There may be a increase in stopping distance or trailer instability which could result in personal injury.

RECREATIONAL TOWING (BEHIND MOTORHOME, ETC.)

Towing This Vehicle Behind Another Vehicle

Towing Condition	Wheels OFF The Ground	Two-Wheel Drive Models	Four-Wheel Drive Models
Flat Tow	NONE	NOT ALLOWED	See Instructions: • Automatic transmission in PARK • Manual transmission in gear (NOT in NEUTRAL) • Transfer case in NEU-TRAL (N) • Tow in forward direction
Dolly Tow	Front	NOT AL-LOWED	NOT ALLOWED
	Rear	OK	NOT ALLOWED
On Trailer	ALL	OK	OK

UTILITY

Recreational Towing – Two-Wheel Drive Models

- **DO NOT flat tow this vehicle. Damage to the drivetrain will result.**

- Recreational towing (for two-wheel drive models) is allowed ONLY if the rear wheels are OFF the ground. This may be accomplished using a tow dolly or vehicle trailer. If using a tow dolly, follow this procedure:
  - Properly secure the dolly to the tow vehicle, following the dolly manufacturer's instructions.
  - Drive the rear wheels onto the tow dolly.
  - Firmly set the parking brake. Place automatic transmission in PARK, manual transmission in gear (not in Neutral).
  - Properly secure the rear wheels to the dolly, following the dolly manufacturer's instructions.
  - Remove the key fob from the ignition switch.
  - Install a suitable clamping device, designed for towing, to secure the front wheels in the straight position.

Recreational Towing – Four-Wheel Drive Models

NOTE:

Both the manual shift and electronic shift transfer cases must be shifted into NEUTRAL (N) for recreational towing. Automatic transmissions must be shifted into PARK for recreational towing. Manual transmissions must be placed in gear (NOT in NEUTRAL) for recreational towing. Refer to the following for the proper transfer case NEUTRAL (N) shifting procedure for your vehicle.

CAUTION!

- Towing with the rear wheels on the ground will cause severe transmission damage. Damage from improper towing is not covered under the New Vehicle Limited Warranty.
- Do not disconnect the driveshaft because fluid may leak from the transmission, causing damage to internal parts.
- Front or rear wheel lifts should not be used. Internal damage to the transmission or transfer case will occur if a front or rear wheel lift is used when recreational towing.
- Tow only in the forward direction. Towing this vehicle backwards can cause severe damage to the transfer case.
- Automatic transmissions must be placed in the PARK position for recreational towing.
- Manual transmissions must be placed in gear (not in Neutral) for recreational towing.
- Before recreational towing, perform the procedure outlined under "Shifting Into NEUTRAL" to be certain that the transfer case is fully in NEUTRAL. Otherwise, internal damage will result.
- Towing this vehicle in violation of the above requirements can cause severe transmission and/or transfer case damage. Damage from improper towing is not covered under the New Vehicle Limited Warranty.
- Do not disconnect the rear driveshaft because fluid will leak from the transfer case, causing damage to internal parts.
- Do not use a bumper-mounted clamp-on tow bar on your vehicle. The bumper face bar will be damaged.

DIESEL

DIESEL ENGINE BREAK-IN RECOMMENDATIONS

- The Cummins® turbocharged diesel engine does not require a break-in period due to its construction. Normal operation is allowed, providing the following recommendations are followed:
  - Warm up the engine before placing it under load.
  - Do not operate the engine at idle for prolonged periods.
  - Use the appropriate transmission gear to prevent engine lugging.
  - Observe vehicle oil pressure and temperature indicators.
  - Check the coolant and oil levels frequently.
  - Vary throttle position at highway speeds when carrying or towing significant weight.

NOTE:
Light duty operation such as light trailer towing or no load operation will extend the time before the engine is at full efficiency. Reduced fuel economy and power may be seen at this time.

- Because of the construction of the Cummins® turbocharged diesel engine, engine run-in is enhanced by loaded operating conditions which allow the engine parts to achieve final finish and fit during the first 6,000 miles (10 000 km).

DIESEL ENGINE STARTING PROCEDURES

Engine Block Heater

- For ambient temperatures below 0°F (-18°C), engine block heater usage is recommended.

- For ambient temperatures below –20°F (-29°C), engine block heater usage is required.

- The engine block heater cord is routed under the hood to the right side and can be located just behind the grille near the headlamp.

- Connect the heater cord to a ground-fault interrupter protected 110–115 volt AC electrical outlet with a grounded, three-wire extension cord.

NOTE:
The block heater will require 110 volts AC and 6.5 amps to activate the heater element.

- The block heater must be plugged in at least one hour to have an adequate warming effect on the coolant.

Water In Fuel Message

- If a Water In Fuel message or 🔋💧 indicator appears in the cluster and a chime sounds five times, the fuel/water separator will need to be drained immediately to prevent engine damage.

- Refer to "Draining Fuel Water Separator" in this guide for draining instructions or see your dealer.

Cold Start Procedure

- Turn the ignition switch to the ON position. If the Wait To Start ᴒᴒ light appears in the cluster, wait for the light to turn off before starting.

- In extremely cold weather below 0°F (-18°C) it may be beneficial to cycle the manifold heaters twice before attempting to start the engine. This can be accomplished by turning the ignition OFF for at least five seconds and then back ON after the "Wait To Start Light" has turned off, but before the engine is started. However, excessive cycling of the manifold heaters will result in damage to the heater elements or reduced battery voltage.

- Refer to the Owner's Manual Diesel Supplement on the DVD for further details.

Engine Idling

- Avoid prolonged engine idling. Long periods of idling may be harmful to your engine because combustion chamber temperatures can drop so low that the fuel may not burn completely.

- Incomplete combustion allows carbon and varnish to form on piston rings, engine valves, and injector nozzles. Also, the unburned fuel can enter the crankcase, diluting the oil and causing rapid wear to the engine.

- If the engine is allowed to idle, under some conditions the idle speed may increase to 900 RPM then return to normal idle speed. This is normal operation.

WARNING!

Remember to disconnect the cord before driving. Damage to the 110–115 volt electrical cord could cause electrocution.

DIESEL EXHAUST BRAKE (ENGINE BRAKING)

- The exhaust brake feature will only function when the driver presses the exhaust brake switch.

- The switch is located on the switch bank below the audio system.

- Your vehicle is also equipped with the Smart Brake feature.

- This feature will automatically provide a variable amount of engine braking in an attempt to maintain a constant vehicle speed.

- The Smart Brake is activated by pressing the exhaust brake switch twice. The first press activate the full strength brake, second press activates the Smart Brake and third press turns the brake off.

- The Smart Brake target vehicle speed is set when either the vehicle brake or the throttle pedal is released.

- Exhaust braking is most effective when the engine RPM is higher.

NOTE:
For optimum braking power, it is recommended to use the exhaust brake while in TOW/HAUL mode.

CAUTION!

Use of aftermarket exhaust brakes is not recommended and could lead to engine damage.

WARNING!

Do not use the exhaust brake feature when driving in icy or slippery conditions as the increased engine braking can cause the rear wheels to slide and the vehicle to swing around with the possible loss of vehicle control, which may cause a collision possibly resulting in personal injury or death.

IDLE-UP FEATURE (AUTOMATIC TRANSMISSION ONLY)

- The Idle-Up Feature uses the speed control switches to increase engine idle speed and quickly warm the vehicle's interior. This feature must be enabled by your dealer. See your local dealer.

- With the transmission in PARK, the parking brake applied, and the engine running, push the speed control ON/OFF switch on, then push the SET switch.

- The engine RPM will go up to 1100 RPM. To increase the RPM, push and hold the RESUME/ACCEL switch and the idle speed will increase to approximately 1500 RPM. To decrease the RPM, push and hold the SET/DECEL switch and the idle speed will decrease to approximately 1100 RPM.

- To cancel the Idle Up Feature, either push the CANCEL switch, push the ON/OFF switch or push the brake pedal.

ENGINE MOUNTED FUEL FILTER/WATER SEPARATOR

Draining Fuel/Water Separator

- If the "Water in Fuel" indicator light 🔋 is illuminated and an audible chime is heard five times, you should stop the engine and drain the water from the separator.
- The drain is located on the bottom of the Fuel Filter and Water Separator assembly which is located on the driver's side of the engine.
- Turn the drain valve (located on the side of the filter) counterclockwise 1/4 turn, then turn the ignition switch to the ON/RUN position to allow any accumulated water to drain.
- When clean fuel is visible, close the drain and switch the ignition to OFF.
- Refer to the Owner's Manual on the DVD for further details.

Fuel Filter Replacement

- With the engine off and a drain pan under the fuel filter drain hose, open the water drain valve 1/4 turn counterclockwise and completely drain fuel and water into the approved container.
- Close the water drain valve and remove the lid using a socket or strap wrench; rotate counterclockwise for removal. Remove the used o-ring and discard it.
- Remove the used filter cartridge from the housing and dispose of according to your local regulations.
- Wipe clean the sealing surfaces of the lid and housing and install the new o-ring into ring groove on the filter housing and lubricate with clean engine oil.
- Install a new filter in the housing. Push down on the cartridge to ensure it is properly seated. **Do not pre-fill the filter housing with fuel.**
- Install the lid onto the housing and tighten to 22.5 ft lbs (30.5 N·m). Do not overtighten the lid.
- Start the engine and confirm no leaks are present.

CAUTION!

- Diesel fuel will damage blacktop paving surfaces. Drain the filter into an appropriate container.
- Do not prefill the fuel filter when installing a new fuel filter. There is a possibility debris could be introduced into the fuel filter during this action. It is best to install the filter dry and allow the in-tank lift pump to prime the fuel system.
- If the "Water In Fuel Indicator Light" remains on, DO NOT START the engine before you drain water from the fuel filter to avoid engine damage.

DIESEL

UNDERBODY MOUNTED FUEL FILTER/WATER SEPARATOR

Draining Fuel/Water Separator

• If the "Water in Fuel" indicator light ⛽ is illuminated and an audible chime is heard five times, you should stop the engine and drain the water from the separator.

• The drain is located on the bottom of the Fuel Filter and Water Separator assembly which is located in front of the rear axle above the drive shaft. The best access to this water drain valve is from under the vehicle.

• Turn the drain valve (located on the side of the filter) counterclockwise 1 full turn, then turn the ignition switch to the ON/RUN position to allow any accumulated water to drain.

• When clean fuel is visible, close the drain and switch the ignition to OFF.

• Refer to the Owner's Manual on the DVD for further details.

Underbody Fuel Filter Replacement

• With the engine off and a drain pan under the fuel filter drain hose, open the water drain valve 1 full turn counterclockwise and completely drain fuel and water into the approved container.

• Close the water drain valve and remove the lid using a socket or strap wrench; rotate counterclockwise for removal. Remove the used o-ring and discard it.

• Remove the used filter cartridge from the housing and dispose of according to your local regulations.

• Wipe clean the sealing surfaces of the lid and housing and install the new o-ring into ring groove on the filter housing and lubricate with clean engine oil.

• Install a new filter in the housing. Push down on the cartridge to ensure it is properly seated. **Do not pre-fill the filter housing with fuel.**

• Start the engine and confirm no leaks are present.

The underbody mounted filter housing is equipped with a No-Filter-No-Run (NFNR) feature. Engine will not run if:

1. No filter is installed.

2. Inferior/Non-approved filter is used. Use of OEM filter is required to ensure vehicle will run.

NOTE:

• Using a fuel filter that does not meet the manufacturer's filtration and water separating requirements can severely impact fuel system life and reliability.

• The WIF sensor is re-usable. Service kit comes with new o-ring for filter canister and WIF sensor.

DIESEL

CAUTION!

- Diesel fuel will damage blacktop paving surfaces. Drain the filter into an appropriate container.
- Do not prefill the fuel filter when installing a new fuel filter. There is a possibility debris could be introduced into the fuel filter during this action. It is best to install the filter dry and allow the in-tank lift pump to prime the fuel system.
- If the "Water In Fuel Indicator Light" remains on, DO NOT START the engine before you drain water from the fuel filter to avoid engine damage.

ADDING FUEL – DIESEL ENGINE ONLY

- Your vehicle is equipped with a cap-less fuel system.
- Most fuel cans will not open the flapper door.
- A funnel is provided to open the flapper door to allow emergency refueling with a fuel can.

Emergency Gas Can Refueling

1. Retrieve funnel from the jack storage area under the passenger seat.
2. Insert the funnel into same filler pipe opening as the fuel nozzle.
3. Ensure the funnel is inserted fully to hold flapper door open.
4. Pour fuel into funnel opening.
5. Remove the funnel from filler pipe, clean off prior to putting back in the jack storage area under the passenger seat.

EXHAUST REGENERATION

- Under certain conditions, your Cummins® diesel engine and exhaust after-treatment system may never reach the conditions required to remove the trapped particulate matter. If this occurs, the "Exhaust System — Regeneration Required Now" message will be displayed on the EVIC screen in your cluster and you will hear one chime to alert you of this condition. Driving your vehicle at highway speeds for as little as 45 minutes can remedy the condition and allow the engine and exhaust after-treatment system to remove the trapped particulate matter.
- PLEASE NOTE: Under typical operating conditions, NO indications of regeneration state will be displayed. If you do reach 80% of filter capacity, the following messages will assist you in inducing and understanding the regeneration process.

Perform Service

- Your vehicle will require emissions maintenance at a set interval. To help remind you when this maintenance is due, the Electronic Vehicle Information Center (EVIC) will display "Perform Service". When the "Perform Service" message is displayed on the EVIC it is necessary to have the emissions maintenance performed. Emissions maintenance may include replacing the Closed Crankcase Ventilation (CCV) filter element, and cleaning of the EGR Cooler. The procedure for clearing and resetting the "Perform Service" indicator message is located in the appropriate Service Information.

Exhaust System — Regeneration Required Now

- "Exhaust System—Regeneration Required Now" will be displayed on the EVIC if the exhaust particulate filter reaches 80% of its maximum storage capacity.

Exhaust Filter XX% Full

- Indicates that the Diesel Particulate Filter (DPF) is approaching full.

Exhaust System — Regeneration in Process

- Indicates that the Diesel Particulate Filter (DPF) is self-cleaning. Maintain your current driving condition until regeneration is completed.

Exhaust System — Regeneration Completed

- Indicates that the Diesel Particulate Filter (DPF) self-cleaning is completed. If this message is displayed, you will hear one chime to assist in alerting you of this condition.

Exhaust Service Required — See Dealer Now

- Regeneration has been disabled due to a system malfunction. The Powertrain control Module (PCM) will register a fault code and the instrument panel will display the MIL light.

Exhaust Filter Full — Power Reduced See Dealer

- The PCM derates the engine in order to limit the likelihood of permanent damage to the after-treatment system. If this condition is not corrected and a dealer service is not performed, extensive exhaust after-treatment damage can occur. Have your vehicle serviced by your local authorized dealer.

CAUTION!

See your authorized dealer, as damage to the exhaust system could occur soon with continued operation.

COOL-DOWN IDLE CHART

TURBO "COOL DOWN" CHART			
Driving Conditions	Load	Turbo Temp	Idle Time (in minutes) Before Shut Down
Stop and Go	Empty	Cool	Less than 1
Stop and Go	Medium	Warm	1
Highway Speeds	Medium	Warm	2
City Traffic	Max. GCWR	Warm	3
Highway Speeds	Max. GCWR	Warm	4
Uphill Grade	Max. GCWR	Hot	5

DIESEL EXHAUST FLUID

- Diesel Exhaust Fluid (DEF) sometimes known simply by the name of its active component, UREA—is a key component of selective catalytic reduction (SCR) systems, which help diesel vehicles meet stringent emission regulations. DEF is a liquid reducing agent that reacts with engine exhaust in the presence of a catalyst to convert smog-forming nitrogen oxides (NOx) into harmless nitrogen and water vapor.

- Your vehicle is equipped with a Selective Catalytic Reduction system in order to meet the very stringent diesel emissions standards required by the Environmental Protection Agency. Selective Catalytic Reduction (SCR) is the first and only technology in decades to be as good for the environment as it is good for business and vehicle performance.

- The purpose of the SCR system is to reduce levels of NOx (oxides of nitrogen emitted from engines) that are harmful to our health and the environment to an almost near-zero level. Small quantities of Diesel Exhaust Fluid (DEF) are injected into the exhaust upstream of a catalyst where, when vaporized, convert smog-forming nitrogen oxides (NOx) into harmless nitrogen (N_2) and water vapor (H_2O), two natural components of the air we breathe. You can operate with the comfort that your vehicle is contributing to a cleaner, healthier world environment for this and generations to come.

System Overview

- This vehicle is equipped with a Diesel Exhaust Fluid (DEF) injection system and a Selective Catalytic Reduction (SCR) catalyst to meet the emission requirements.

- The DEF injection system consists of the following components:
  - DEF tank
  - DEF pump
  - DEF injector
  - Electronically-heated DEF lines
  - DEF control module
  - NOx sensors

DIESEL

- NH3 sensor
- Temperature sensors
- SCR catalyst

- The DEF injection system and SCR catalyst enable the achievement of diesel emissions requirements; while maintaining outstanding fuel economy, drivability, torque and power ratings.

NOTE:

- Your vehicle is equipped with a DEF injection system. You may occasionally hear an audible clicking noise. This is normal operation.

- The DEF pump will run for a period of time after engine shutdown to purge the DEF system. This is normal operation.

Diesel Exhaust Fluid Storage

- Diesel Exhaust Fluid (DEF) is considered a very stable product with a long shelf life. If DEF is kept in temperatures between 10° to 90°F (-12° to 32°C), it will last a minimum of one year.

- DEF is subject to freezing at the lowest temperatures. For example, DEF may freeze at temperatures at or below 12° F (-11° C). The system has been designed to operate in this environment.

NOTE:

When working with DEF, it is important to know that:

- Any containers or parts that come into contact with DEF must be DEF compatible (plastic or stainless steel). Copper, brass, aluminum, iron or non-stainless steel should be avoided as they are subject to corrosion by DEF.

- If DEF is spilled, it should be wiped up completely.

Adding Diesel Exhaust Fluid

- The DEF gauge (located in the instrument cluster) will display the level of DEF remaining in the tank.

NOTE:

Driving conditions (altitude, vehicle speed, load, etc.) will effect the amount of DEF that is used in your vehicle.

DEF Fill Procedure

- Remove cap from DEF tank (located on drivers side of the vehicle).

- Insert DEF container into DEF tank.
- Reinstall cap onto DEF tank.
- Refer to your Owner's Manual on the DVD for further details.

CAUTION!

- To avoid DEF spillage and overfilling, do not "top off" the DEF tank after filling.
- When DEF is spilled, clean the area immediately with water or a mild solvent.

WHAT TO DO IN EMERGENCIES

ROADSIDE ASSISTANCE

- Dial toll-free 1-800-521-2779 for U.S. Residents or 1-800-363-4869 for Canadian Residents.

- Provide your name, vehicle identification number, license plate number, and your location, including the telephone number from which you are calling.

- Briefly describe the nature of the problem and answer a few simple questions.

- You will be given the name of the service provider and an estimated time of arrival. If you feel you are in an "unsafe situation", please let us know. With your consent, we will contact local police or safety authorities.

INSTRUMENT CLUSTER WARNING LIGHTS

⛙ - Electronic Stability Control (ESC) Activation/Malfunction Indicator Light

- If this indicator light flashes during acceleration, apply as little throttle as possible. While driving, ease up on the accelerator. Adapt your speed and driving to the prevailing road conditions. To improve the vehicle's traction when starting off in deep snow, sand or gravel, it may be desirable to switch the ESC system off.

(!) - Tire Pressure Monitoring System (TPMS) Light

- Each tire, including the spare (if provided), should be checked monthly, when cold and inflated to the inflation pressure recommended by the vehicle manufacturer on the vehicle placard or tire inflation pressure label. (If your vehicle has tires of a different size than the size indicated on the vehicle placard or tire inflation pressure label, you should determine the proper tire inflation pressure for those tires.)

- As an added safety feature, your vehicle has been equipped with a Tire Pressure Monitoring System (TPMS) that illuminates a low tire pressure telltale when one or more of your tires is significantly under-inflated. Accordingly, when the low tire pressure telltale illuminates, you should stop and check your tires as soon as possible, and inflate them to the proper pressure. Driving on a significantly under-inflated tire causes the tire to overheat and can lead to tire failure. Under-inflation also reduces fuel efficiency and tire tread life, and may affect the vehicle's handling and stopping ability.

- **IF THE LIGHT STARTS FLASHING INDICATING A LOW TIRE PRESSURE, ADJUST THE AIR PRESSURE IN THE LOW TIRE TO THE AIR PRESSURE SHOWN ON THE VEHICLE PLACARD OR TIRE INFLATION PRESSURE LABEL LOCATED ON THE DRIVER'S DOOR. NOTE: AFTER INFLATION, THE VEHICLE MAY NEED TO BE DRIVEN FOR 20 MINUTES BEFORE THE FLASHING LIGHT WILL TURN OFF.**

- Please note that the TPMS is not a substitute for proper tire maintenance, and it is the driver's responsibility to maintain correct tire pressure, even if under-inflation has not reached the level to trigger illumination of the TPMS low tire pressure telltale.

- Your vehicle has also been equipped with a TPMS malfunction indicator to indicate when the system is not operating properly. The TPMS malfunction indicator is

WHAT TO DO IN EMERGENCIES

combined with the low tire pressure telltale. When the system detects a malfunction, the telltale will flash for approximately one minute and then remain continuously illuminated. This sequence will continue each time the vehicle is restarted as long as the malfunction exists.

• When the malfunction indicator is illuminated, the system may not be able to detect or signal low tire pressure as intended. TPMS malfunctions may occur for a variety of reasons, including the installation of replacement or alternate tires or wheels on the vehicle that prevent the TPMS from functioning properly. Always check the TPMS malfunction telltale after replacing one or more tires or wheels on your vehicle, to ensure that the replacement or alternate tires and wheels allow the TPMS to continue to function properly.

NOTE:
Tire pressures change by approximately 1 psi (7 kPa) per 12° F (7° C) of air temperature change. Keep this in mind when checking tire pressure inside a garage, especially in the Winter. Example: If garage temperature is 68°F (20°C) and the outside temperature is 32°F (0°C), then the cold tire inflation pressure should be increased by 3 psi (21 kPa), which equals 1 psi (7 kPa) for every 12°F (7°C) for this outside temperature condition.

CAUTION!

The TPMS has been optimized for the original equipment tires and wheels. TPMS pressures and warning have been established for the tire size equipped on your vehicle. Undesirable system operation or sensor damage may result when using replacement equipment that is not of the same size, type, and/or style. Aftermarket wheels can cause sensor damage. Do not use tire sealant from a can, or balance beads if your vehicle is equipped with a TPMS, as damage to the sensors may result.

⚖ - Engine Temperature Warning Light

• This light warns of an overheated engine condition.
• If the light turns on and a warning chime sounds while driving, safely pull over and stop the vehicle. If the A/C system is on, turn it off. Also, shift the transmission into NEUTRAL and idle the vehicle. If the temperature reading does not return to normal, turn the engine off immediately.
• We recommend that you do not operate the vehicle or engine damage will occur. Have the vehicle serviced immediately.

WARNING!

A hot engine cooling system is dangerous. You or others could be badly burned by steam or boiling coolant. You may want to call an authorized dealer for service if your vehicle overheats.

WHAT TO DO IN EMERGENCIES

BRAKE - Brake Warning Light

- The Brake Warning light illuminates when there is either a system malfunction or the parking brake is applied. If the light is on and the parking brake is not applied, it indicates a possible brake hydraulic malfunction, brake booster problem or an Anti-Lock Brake System problem.

- Please have your vehicle serviced immediately.

WARNING!

Driving a vehicle with the red brake light on is dangerous. Part of the brake system may have failed. It will take longer to stop the vehicle. You could have a collision. Have the vehicle checked immediately.

- Malfunction Indicator Light (MIL)

- Certain conditions, such as a loose or missing gas cap, poor fuel quality, etc., may illuminate the MIL after engine start. The vehicle should be serviced if the light stays on through several typical driving cycles. In most situations, the vehicle will drive normally and not require towing.

- If the MIL flashes when the engine is running, serious conditions may exist that could lead to immediate loss of power or severe catalytic converter damage. We recommend you do not operate the vehicle. Have the vehicle serviced immediately.

- Electronic Stability Control (ESC) OFF Indicator Light

- If the ESC OFF indicator light comes on when the Electronic Stability Control (ESC) is off.

- Charging System Light

- This light shows the status of the electrical charging system. If the charging system light remains on, it means that the vehicle is experiencing a problem with the charging system.

- We recommend you do not continue driving if the charging system light is on. Have the vehicle serviced immediately.

- Oil Pressure Warning Light

- This light indicates low engine oil pressure. If the light turns on while driving, stop the vehicle and shut off the engine as soon as possible. A chime will sound for four minutes when this light turns on.

- We recommend you do not operate the vehicle or engine damage will occur. Have the vehicle serviced immediately.

(ABS) - Anti-Lock Brake (ABS) Light

- This light monitors the Anti-Lock Brake System (ABS).

- If the light is not on during starting, stays on, or turns on while driving, we recommend you drive to the nearest service center and have the vehicle serviced immediately.

🖐 - Electronic Throttle Control (ETC) Light

- This light informs you of a problem with the Electronic Throttle Control (ETC) system.

- If a problem is detected, the light will come on while the engine is running. Cycle the ignition when the vehicle has completely stopped and the shift lever is placed in the PARK position; the light should turn off.

- If the light remains lit with the engine running, your vehicle will usually be drivable; however, see an authorized service center immediately. If the light is flashing when the engine is running, immediate service is required and you may experience reduced performance, an elevated/rough idle or engine stall and your vehicle may require towing.

🏃 - Air Bag Warning Light

- If the light is not on during starting, stays on, or turns on while driving, have the vehicle serviced by an authorized service center immediately.

SVC/4WD - SVC (Service) 4WD Indicator Light

- The SVC 4WD light monitors the electric shift four-wheel drive system. If the SVC 4WD light stays on or comes on during driving, it means that the four-wheel drive system is not functioning properly and that service is required.

- For vehicles equipped with a premium cluster this indicator will display in the Electronic Vehicle Information Center (EVIC).

⊕ - Transmission Temperature Warning Light

- This light indicates that there is excessive transmission fluid temperature that might occur with severe usage such as trailer towing. If this light turns on, stop the vehicle and run the engine at idle, with the transmission in NEUTRAL, until the light turns off. Once the light turns off, you may continue to drive normally.

OIL CHANGE EVIC INDICATOR

Message

- If an "oil change" message (shown as "Change Oil Soon" and "Oil Change Needed") appears and a single chime sounds, it is time for your next required oil change.

Resetting The Light After Servicing

- Turn the ignition switch to the ON/RUN position (do not start engine).
- Fully depress the accelerator pedal three times within 10 seconds.
- Turn the ignition switch to the OFF/LOCK position.

🛢 - Low Coolant Level Indicator Light

- This light indicates low coolant level. If the light turns on while driving, stop the vehicle and shut off the engine as soon as possible.

- We recommend you do not operate the vehicle or engine damage will occur. Have the vehicle serviced immediately.

WHAT TO DO IN EMERGENCIES

IF YOUR ENGINE OVERHEATS

- In any of the following situations, you can reduce the potential for overheating by taking the appropriate action.
- On the highways — slow down.
- In city traffic — while stopped, place the transmission in NEUTRAL, but do not increase engine idle speed.

NOTE:
There are steps that you can take to slow down an impending overheat condition:

- If your air conditioner (A/C) is on, turn it off. The A/C system adds heat to the engine cooling system and turning the A/C off can help remove this heat.
- You can also turn the temperature control to maximum heat, the mode control to floor and the blower control to high. This allows the heater core to act as a supplement to the radiator and aids in removing heat from the engine cooling system.

CAUTION!

Driving with a hot cooling system could damage your vehicle. If the temperature gauge reads HOT (H), pull over and stop the vehicle. Idle the vehicle with the air conditioner turned off until the pointer drops back into the normal range. If the pointer remains on HOT (H), and you hear continuous chimes, turn the engine off immediately, and call for service.

WARNING!

You or others can be badly burned by hot engine coolant (antifreeze) or steam from your radiator. If you see or hear steam coming from under the hood, do not open the hood until the radiator has had time to cool. Never try to open a cooling system pressure cap when the radiator or coolant bottle is hot.

JACKING AND TIRE CHANGING

Jack Location

- The jack and jack tools are stored under the front passenger seat.

Removal Of Jack And Tools

- To access the jack and jack tools you must remove the plastic access cover, located on the side of the seat. To remove the cover, pull the front part of the cover (closest to the front of the seat) toward you to release a locking tab. Once the front of the cover is loose, slide the cover toward the front of the seat until it is free from the seat frame.

Jack & Tire Changing Tools Behind Cover

1500 Series Trucks

- Remove the jack and tool bag by removing the wing bolt and sliding the jack and tool bag from under the seat.

2500/3500 Series Trucks

- Remove the jack and tool bracket assembly by removing the wing bolt and sliding the jack and tool bracket assembly from under the seat.

WHAT TO DO IN EMERGENCIES

Removing The Spare Tire

• Remove the spare tire before attempting to jack up the truck. Attach the wheel wrench to the jack extension tube. Insert the tube through the access hole between the lower tailgate and the top of the bumper and into the winch mechanism tube. Rotate the wheel wrench handle counterclockwise until the spare tire is on the ground with enough cable slack to allow you to pull it out from under the vehicle. When the spare is clear, tilt the retainer at the end of the cable and pull it through the center of the wheel.

NOTE:
Always stow the spare tire with the valve stem facing the ground.

1. Wheel Wrench

2. Spare Tire

• It is recommended that you stow the flat or spare to avoid tangling the loose cable.

NOTE:
The winch mechanism is designed for use with the jack extension tube only. Use of an air wrench or other power tools is not recommended and can damage the winch.

Preparations

1. Park the vehicle on a firm, level surface. Avoid ice or slippery areas.

2. Turn on the Hazard Warning flasher.

3. Set the parking brake.

4. Place the shift lever into PARK. On four-wheel drive vehicles, shift the transfer case to the 4L position.

5. Turn the ignition OFF.

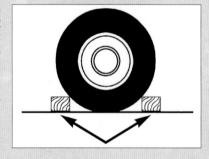

• Block both the front and rear of the wheel diagonally opposite the jacking position. For example, if the right front wheel is being changed, block the left rear wheel.

NOTE:
Passengers should not remain in the vehicle when the vehicle is being jacked.

Instructions

1. Remove the spare wheel, jack, and tools from storage.

2. Using the wheel wrench, loosen, but do not remove, the wheel nuts by turning them counterclockwise one turn while the wheel is still on the ground.

3. Placement of the jack:

1500 Series Trucks

• When changing a front wheel, place the scissors jack under the rear portion of the lower control arm as shown below.

Front 4x2 Jacking Location

Front 4x4 Jacking Location

- Operate the jack using the jack drive tube and the wheel wrench. The tube extension may be used but is not required.

- **For 4x2 and 4x4 trucks**, when changing a rear wheel, assemble the jack drive tube to the jack and connect the drive tube to the extension tube. Place the jack under the axle between the wheel and the shock bracket with the drive tubes extending to the rear.

Rear 4x4 Jacking Location

- Connect the jack tube extension and wheel wrench.

WHAT TO DO IN EMERGENCIES

2500/3500 Series Trucks

• **For 2500/3500 4x2 series trucks,** when changing a front wheel, place the bottle jack under the frame rail behind the wheel. Locate the jack as far forward as possible on the straight part of the frame.

• Operate the jack using the jack drive tube and the wheel wrench. The tube extension, may be used, but is not required.

- **For 2500/3500 4x4 series trucks,** when changing the front wheel, assemble the jack drive tube to the jack and connect the drive tube to the extension tube. Place the jack under the axle as close to the tire as possible with the drive tubes extending to the front. Connect the jack tube extension and wheel wrench.

- **For 4x2 and 4x4 trucks**, when changing a rear wheel, assemble the jack drive tube to the jack and connect the drive tube to the extension tube. Place the jack under the axle between the spring and the shock absorber with the drive tubes extending to the rear.

- Connect the jack tube extension and wheel wrench.

NOTE:
If the bottle jack will not lower by turning the dial (thumbwheel) by hand, it may be necessary to use the jack drive tube in order to lower the jack.

- By rotating the wheel wrench clockwise, raise the vehicle until the wheel just clears the surface.

- Remove the wheel nuts and pull the wheel off. On single rear-wheel (SRW) trucks, install the spare wheel and wheel nuts with the cone shaped end of the wheel nuts toward the wheel. On 3500 dual rear-wheel models (DRW) the wheel nuts are a two-piece assembly with a flat face. Lightly tighten the wheel nuts. To avoid the risk of forcing the vehicle off the jack, do not fully tighten the wheel nuts until the vehicle has been lowered.

- Using the lug wrench, finish tightening the wheel nuts using a crisscross pattern. The correct wheel nut tightness is 130 ft lbs (175 N·m) torque (1500 Series), 135 ft lbs (183 N·m) torque for 2500/3500 single-rear wheel (SRW) models, and 140 ft lbs (190 N·m) for 3500 dual rear-wheel models. If in doubt about the correct tightness, have them checked with a torque wrench by your authorized dealer or at a service station.

- Install the wheel center cap and remove the wheel blocks. Do not install chrome or aluminum wheel center caps on the spare wheel. This may result in cap damage.

WHAT TO DO IN EMERGENCIES

- Lower the jack to its fully closed position. If the bottle jack will not lower by turning the dial (thumbwheel) by hand, it may be necessary to use the jack drive tube in order to lower the jack. Stow the replaced tire, jack, and tools as previously described.
- Adjust the tire pressure when possible.

NOTE:

Do not oil wheel studs. For chrome wheels, do not substitute with chrome plated wheel nuts.

Reinstalling The Jack And Tools

1500 Series Trucks

1. Tighten the jack all the way down by turning the jack turn-screw clockwise until the jack is snug.

2. Position the jack and tool bag. Make sure the lug wrench is under the jack near the jack turn-screw.

3. Secure the tool bag straps to the jack.

4. Place the jack and tools in the storage position holding the jack by the jack turn-screw, slip the jack and tools under the seat so that the bottom slot engages into the fastener on the floor.

NOTE:

Ensure that the jack slides into the front hold down location.

5. Turn the wing bolt clockwise to secure to the floor pan. Reinstall the plastic cover.

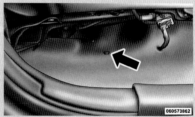

2500/3500 Series Trucks

1. Tighten the jack all the way down by turning the jack turn-screw clockwise until the jack is snug.

2. Position the jack and tools into bracket assembly. Make sure the lug wrench is under the jack near the jack turn-screw. Snap tools into bracket assembly clips. Install the jack into bracket assembly and turn screw until jack is snug into bracket assembly.

3. Place the jack and tool bracket assembly in the storage position holding the jack by the jack turn-screw, slip the jack and tools under the seat so that the bottom slot engages into the fastener on the floor.

NOTE:

Ensure that the jack and tool bracket assembly slides into the front hold down location.

4. Turn the wing bolt clockwise to secure to the floor pan. Reinstall the plastic cover.

Hub Caps/Wheel Covers

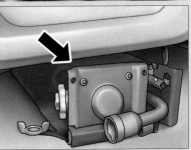

- The hub caps must be removed before raising the vehicle off the ground.

- For single rear-wheel (SRW) models, use the blade on the end of the lug wrench to pry the hub cap off. Insert the blade end into the pry-off notch and carefully pop off the hub cap with a back-and-forth motion.

- On models with dual rear wheels (DRW), you must first remove the hub caps. The jack handle driver has a hook at one end that will fit in the pry off notch of the rear hub caps. Position the hook and pull out on the ratchet firmly. The hub cap should pop off. The wheel skins can now be removed. For the front hub cap use the blade on the end of the lug wrench to pry the caps off. The wheel skin can now be removed.

- You must use the flat end of the lug wrench to pry off the wheel skins. Insert the flat tip completely and using a back-and-forth motion, loosen the wheel skin. Repeat this procedure around the tire until the skin pops off.

WHAT TO DO IN EMERGENCIES

- Replace the wheel skins first using a rubber mallet. When replacing the hub caps, tilt the cap retainer over the lug nut bolt circle and strike the high side down with a rubber mallet. Be sure that the hub caps and wheel skins are firmly seated around the wheel.

Wheel Nuts

- All wheel nuts should be tightened occasionally to eliminate the possibility of wheel studs being sheared or the bolt holes in the wheels becoming elongated. This is especially important during the first few hundred miles/kilometers of operation to allow the wheel nuts to become properly set. All wheel nuts should first be firmly seated against the wheel. The wheel nuts should then be tightened to recommended torque. Tighten the wheel nuts to final torque in increments. Progress around the bolt circle, tightening the wheel nut opposite to the wheel nut just previously tightened until final torque is achieved. Recommended torques are shown in the following chart.

Disc Wheels

Nut Type	Stud Size	Hex Size	Torque Ft Lbs	Torque Newton Meters
Cone	M14 x 1.5	22 mm	120-140	160-190
Flanged	M14 x 1.5	22 mm	130-160	175-215

8-Stud — Dual Rear Wheels

- Dual wheels are flat-mounted and center-piloted. The lug nuts are a two-piece assembly. When the tires are being rotated or replaced, clean these lug nuts and add two drops of oil at the interface between the hex and the washer.

- Slots in the wheels will assist in properly orienting the inner and outer wheels. Align these slots when assembling the wheels for best access to the tire valve on the inner wheel. The tires of both dual wheels must be completely off the ground when tightening, to ensure wheel centering and maximum wheel clamping.

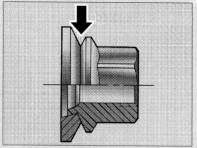

- Dual wheel models require a special heavy-duty lug nut tightening adapter (included with the vehicle) to correctly tighten the lug nuts. Also, when it is necessary to remove and install dual rear wheels, use a proper vehicle lifting device.

NOTE:

When installing a spare tire as part of a dual rear wheel end combination, the tire diameter of the two individual tires must be compared. If there is a significant difference, the larger tire should be installed in a front location. The correct direction of rotation for dual tire installations must also be observed.

These dual rear wheels should be tightened as follows:

1. Tighten the wheel nuts in the numbered sequence to a snug fit.

2. Retighten the wheel nuts in the same sequence to the torques listed in the table. Go through the sequence a second time to verify that specific torque has been achieved. Retighten to specifications at 100 miles (160 km) and after 500 miles (800 km).

• It is recommended that wheel stud nuts be kept torqued to specifications at all times. Torque wheel stud nuts to specifications at each lubrication interval.

To Stow The Flat Or Spare

NOTE:

RAM 1500 vehicles equipped with aluminum wheels cannot be stored under the vehicle because the wheel retainer will not fit through the wheel pilot hole. Secure the flat tire in the bed of the truck. Have the flat tire repaired or replaced immediately.

• Turn the wheel so that the valve stem is down. Slide the wheel retainer through the center of the wheel and position it properly across the wheel opening.

• For convenience in checking the spare tire inflation, stow with the valve stem toward the rear of the vehicle.

• Attach the wheel wrench to the extension tube. Rotate the winch mechanism until the wheel is drawn into place against the underside of the vehicle. Continue to rotate until you feel the winch mechanism slip, or click three or four times. It cannot be overtightened. Push against the tire several times to be sure it is firmly in place.

149

WHAT TO DO IN EMERGENCIES

CAUTION!

- Do not attempt to raise the vehicle by jacking on locations other than those indicated in the Jacking Instructions for this vehicle.
- Before raising the wheel off the ground, make sure that the jack will not damage surrounding truck parts and adjust the jack position as required.
- Use a back and forth motion to remove the hub cap. Do not use a twisting motion when removing the hub cap, damage to the hub cap; finish may occur.
- The rear hub caps on the dual rear wheel has two pry off notches. Make sure that the hook of the jack handle driver is located squarely in the cap notch before attempting to pull off.

WARNING!

- Do not attempt to change a tire on the side of the vehicle close to moving traffic. Pull far enough off the road to avoid the danger of being hit when operating the jack or changing the wheel.
- Being under a jacked-up vehicle is dangerous. The vehicle could slip off the jack and fall on you. You could be crushed. Never put any part of your body under a vehicle that is on a jack.
- Never start or run the engine while the vehicle is on a jack. If you need to get under a raised vehicle, take it to an authorized dealer where it can be raised on a lift.
- The jack is designed to be used as a tool for changing tires only. The jack should not be used to lift the vehicle for service purposes. The vehicle should be jacked on a firm level surface only. Avoid ice or slippery areas.
- Do not attempt to change a tire on the side of the vehicle close to moving traffic, pull far enough off the road to avoid the danger of being hit when operating the jack or changing the wheel.
- Carefully follow these tire changing warnings to help prevent personal injury or damage to your vehicle:
- Always park on a firm, level surface as far from the edge of the roadway as possible before raising the vehicle.
- Turn on the Hazard Warning flashers.
- Block the wheel diagonally opposite the wheel to be raised.
- Set the parking brake firmly and set an automatic transmission in PARK; a manual transmission in REVERSE.
- Do not let anyone sit in the vehicle when it is on a jack.
- Do not get under the vehicle when it is on a jack.
- Only use the jack in the positions indicated and for lifting this vehicle during a tire change.
- If working on or near a roadway, be extremely careful of motor traffic.
- To assure that spare tires, flat or inflated, are securely stowed, spares must be stowed with the valve stem facing the ground.
- Raising the vehicle higher than necessary can make the vehicle less stable. It could slip off the jack and hurt someone near it. Raise the vehicle only enough to remove the tire.
- To avoid the risk of forcing the vehicle off the jack, do not fully tighten the wheel bolts until the vehicle has been lowered. Failure to follow this warning may result in personal injury.
- To avoid possible personal injury, handle the wheel covers with care to avoid contact with any sharp edges.
- A loose tire or jack thrown forward in a collision or hard stop could endanger the occupants of the vehicle. Always stow the jack parts and the spare tire in the places provided.
- A loose tire thrown forward in a collision or hard stop could injure the occupants in the vehicle. Have the deflated (flat) tire repaired or replaced immediately.

WHAT TO DO IN EMERGENCIES

JUMP-STARTING

- If your vehicle has a discharged battery it can be jump-started using a set of jumper cables and a battery in another vehicle or by using a portable battery booster pack.

- Jump-starting can be dangerous if done improperly so please follow the procedures in this section carefully.

NOTE:
When using a portable battery booster pack follow the manufacturer's operating instructions and precautions.

Positive Terminal

Preparations for Jump-Start

- The battery in your vehicle is located in the front of the engine compartment, behind the left headlight assembly.

NOTE:
The positive battery post is covered with a protective cap. Lift up on the cap to gain access to the positive battery post.

- Set the parking brake, shift the automatic transmission into PARK and turn the ignition to LOCK.

- Turn off the heater, radio, and all unnecessary electrical accessories.

- If using another vehicle to jump-start the battery, park the vehicle within the jumper cables reach, set the parking brake and make sure the ignition is OFF.

Jump-Starting Procedure

- Connect the positive (+) end of the jumper cable to the positive (+) post of the discharged vehicle.

- Connect the opposite end of the positive (+) jumper cable to the positive (+) post of the booster battery.

- Connect the negative end (-) of the jumper cable to the negative (-) post of the booster battery.

- Connect the opposite end of the negative (-) jumper cable to a good engine ground (exposed metal part of the discharged vehicle's engine) away from the battery and the fuel injection system.

- Start the engine in the vehicle that has the booster battery, let the engine idle a few minutes, and then start the engine in the vehicle with the discharged battery.

Once the engine is started, remove the jumper cables in the reverse sequence:

- Disconnect the negative (-) jumper cable from the engine ground of the vehicle with the discharged battery.
- Disconnect the negative end (-) of the jumper cable from the negative (-) post of the booster battery.
- Disconnect the opposite end of the positive (+) jumper cable from the positive (+) post of the booster battery.
- Disconnect the positive (+) end of the jumper cable from the positive (+) post of the discharged vehicle.
- If frequent jump-starting is required to start your vehicle you should have the battery and charging system inspected at your authorized dealer.

CAUTION!

- Do not use a portable battery booster pack or any other booster source with a system voltage greater than 12 Volts or damage to the battery, starter motor, alternator or electrical system may occur.
- Failure to follow these procedures could result in damage to the charging system of the booster vehicle or the discharged vehicle.
- Accessories that can be plugged into the vehicle power outlets draw power from the vehicle's battery, even when not in use (i.e., cellular phones, etc.). Eventually, if plugged in long enough, the vehicle's battery will discharge sufficiently to degrade battery life and/or prevent the engine from starting.

WARNING!

- When temperatures are below the freezing point, electrolyte in a discharged battery may freeze. Do not attempt jump-starting because the battery could rupture or explode and cause personal injury. Battery temperature must be brought above the freezing point before attempting a jump-start.
- Take care to avoid the radiator cooling fan whenever the hood is raised. It can start anytime the ignition switch is on. You can be injured by moving fan blades.
- Remove any metal jewelry, such as watch bands or bracelets, that might make an inadvertent electrical contact. You could be severely injured.
- Batteries contain sulfuric acid that can burn your skin or eyes and generate hydrogen gas which is flammable and explosive. Keep open flames or sparks away from the battery.
- Do not allow vehicles to touch each other as this could establish a ground connection and personal injury could result.
- Failure to follow this procedure could result in personal injury or property damage due to battery explosion.
- Do not connect the cable to the negative post (-) of the discharged battery. The resulting electrical spark could cause the battery to explode and could result in personal injury.

WHAT TO DO IN EMERGENCIES

EMERGENCY TOW HOOKS

- If your vehicle is equipped with tow hooks, they are mounted in the front.
- For off-road recovery, it is recommended to use both of the front tow hooks to minimize the risk of damage to the vehicle.

CAUTION!

Tow hooks are for emergency use only, to rescue a vehicle stranded off-road. Do not use tow hooks for tow truck hookup or highway towing. You could damage your vehicle. Tow straps are recommended when towing the vehicle; chains may cause vehicle damage.

WARNING!

- Chains are not recommended for freeing a stuck vehicle. Chains may break, causing serious injury or death.
- Stand clear of vehicles when pulling with tow hooks. Tow straps and chains may break, causing serious injury.

SHIFT LEVER OVERRIDE

- If a malfunction occurs and the shift lever cannot be moved out of the PARK position, you can use the following procedure to temporarily move the shift lever.
- Have your vehicle inspected by your local authorized dealer immediately if the shift lever override has been used.

Column Shifter

- Tilt the steering wheel to the full up position and firmly set the parking brake.
- Turn the Key Fob to the ACC or ON/RUN position without starting the engine.
- Press and maintain firm pressure on the brake pedal.
- Using a screwdriver, press and hold the override tab through the access port (ringed circle) on the bottom of the steering column.
- Move the shift lever into the NEUTRAL position and start the vehicle.
- Release the parking brake.

Shift Lock Manual
Override Access Port

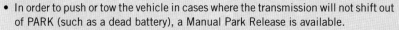

Center Console Shifter

- Firmly set the parking brake.
- Turn the Key Fob to the ACC or ON/RUN position without starting the engine.
- Press and maintain firm pressure on the brake pedal.
- Using a screwdriver, press and hold the override tab through the access port on the center console.
- Move the shift lever into the NEUTRAL position and start the vehicle.
- Release the parking brake.

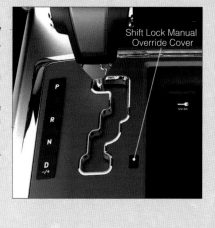

Shift Lock Manual Override Cover

MANUAL PARK RELEASE — EIGHT SPEED TRANSMISSION

- In order to push or tow the vehicle in cases where the transmission will not shift out of PARK (such as a dead battery), a Manual Park Release is available.
- Follow these steps to use the Manual Park Release:
  - Firmly apply the parking brake.

  - Using a small screwdriver or similar tool, remove the Manual Park Release access cover, which is just above the parking brake release handle, below and to the left of the steering column.

Manual Park Release Access Cover

- Using the screwdriver or similar tool, push the Manual Park Release lever locking tab (just below the middle of the lever) to the right.

Manual Park Release Lever Locking Tab

- While holding the locking tab in the disengaged position, pull the tether strap to rotate the lever rearward, until it locks in place pointing towards the driver's seat. Release the locking tab and verify that the Manual Park Release lever is locked in the released position.
- The vehicle is now out of PARK and can be towed. Release the parking brake only when the vehicle is securely connected to a tow vehicle.

To Reset The Manual Park Release:

- Push the locking tab to the right, to unlock the lever.
- Rotate the Manual Park Release lever forward to its original position, until the locking tab snaps into place to secure the lever.

Manual Park Release Tether

- Pull gently on the tether strap to confirm that the lever is locked in its stowed position.
- Re-install the access cover.

WARNING!

Always secure your vehicle by fully applying the parking brake, before activating the Manual Park Release. Activating the Manual Park Release will allow your vehicle to roll away if it is not secured by the parking brake or by proper connection to a tow vehicle. Activating the Manual Park Release on an unsecured vehicle could lead to serious injury or death for those in or around the vehicle.

TOWING A DISABLED VEHICLE

Towing Condition	Wheels OFF the Ground		2WD Models	4WD Models
Flat Tow	NONE		If transmission is operable: • Transmission in **NEUTRAL** • 30 mph (48 km/h) **max** • 15 miles (24 km) **max** distance	• Auto Transmission in **PARK** • Manual Transmission in gear **(NOT NEUTRAL)** • Transfer Case in **NEUTRAL** • Tow in **FORWARD** direction
Wheel Lift or Dolly Tow	Front			**NOT ALLOWED**
	Rear		**OK**	**NOT ALLOWED**
Flatbed	ALL		**BEST METHOD**	**BEST METHOD**

WHAT TO DO IN EMERGENCIES

FREEING A STUCK VEHICLE

• If your vehicle becomes stuck in mud, sand or snow, it can often be moved by a rocking motion. Turn your steering wheel right and left to clear the area around the front wheels. Then, move the shift lever back and forth between REVERSE and DRIVE. Using minimal accelerator pedal pressure to maintain the rocking motion, without spinning the wheels, is most effective.

• Allow the engine to idle with the transmission shift lever in NEUTRAL for at least one minute after every five rocking-motion cycles. This will minimize overheating and reduce the risk of transmission failure during prolonged efforts to free a stuck vehicle.

NOTE:
If your vehicle is equipped with Electronic Stability Control (ESC) then press the "ESC Off" switch, to place the Electronic Stability Control (ESC) system in "Partial Off" mode, before rocking the vehicle.

CAUTION!
Revving the engine or spinning the wheels too fast may lead to transmission overheating and failure. It can also damage the tires. Do not spin the wheels above 30 mph (48 km/h) while in gear (no transmission shifting occurring).

WARNING!
Fast spinning tires can be dangerous. Forces generated by excessive wheel speeds may cause tire damage or failure. A tire could explode and injure someone. Do not spin your vehicle's wheels faster than 30 mph (48 km/h) when you are stuck. Do not let anyone near a spinning wheel, no matter what the speed.

WHAT TO DO IN EMERGENCIES

EVENT DATA RECORDER (EDR)

- This vehicle is equipped with an Event Data Recorder (EDR). The main purpose of an EDR is to record, in certain crash or near crash-like situations, such as an air bag deployment or hitting a road obstacle, data that will assist in understanding how a vehicle's systems performed. The EDR is designed to record data related to vehicle dynamics and safety systems for a short period of time, typically 30 seconds or less. The EDR in this vehicle is designed to record such data as:
  - How various systems in your vehicle were operating;
  - Whether or not the driver and passenger safety belts were buckled/fastened;
  - How far (if at all) the driver was depressing the accelerator and/or brake pedal; and,
  - How fast the vehicle was traveling.

- These data can help provide a better understanding of the circumstances in which crashes and injuries occur.

NOTE:
EDR data are recorded by your vehicle only if a non-trivial crash situation occurs; no data are recorded by the EDR under normal driving conditions and no personal data (e.g. name, gender, age, and crash location) are recorded. However, other parties, such as law enforcement, could combine the EDR data with the type of personally identifying data routinely acquired during a crash investigation.

- To read data recorded by an EDR, special equipment is required, and access to the vehicle or the EDR is needed. In addition to the vehicle manufacturer, other parties such as law enforcement, that have the special equipment, can read the information if they have access to the vehicle or the EDR.

MAINTAINING YOUR VEHICLE

OPENING THE HOOD

- Pull the hood release lever located below the steering wheel at the base of the instrument panel.
- Reach into the opening beneath the center of the hood and move the safety latch lever while lifting the hood at the same time.

Hood Release
(below steering wheel at
base of instrument panel)

WARNING!
Be sure the hood is fully latched before driving your vehicle. If the hood is not fully latched, it could open when the vehicle is in motion and block your vision. Failure to follow this warning could result in serious injury or death.

ENGINE COMPARTMENT

3.6L Engine

Battery

Brake Fluid Reservoir

Engine Oil Fill

Washer Fluid Reservoir

Integrated Power Module (Fuses)

Engine Oil Dipstick

Air Cleaner Filter

Engine Coolant Reservoir

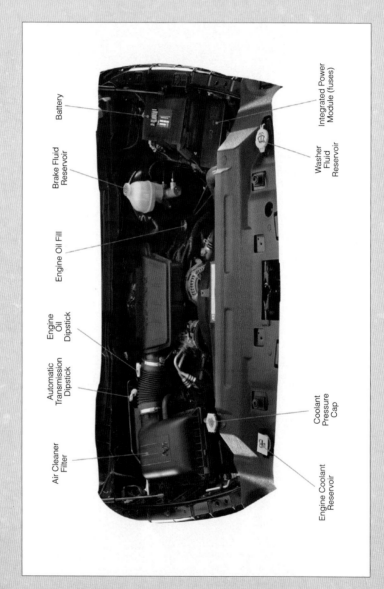

Battery

Brake Fluid Reservoir

Engine Oil Fill

Engine Oil Dipstick

Automatic Transmission Dipstick

Air Cleaner Filter

Integrated Power Module (fuses)

Washer Fluid Reservoir

Coolant Pressure Cap

Engine Coolant Reservoir

4.7L Engine

5.7L ENGINE

Brake Fluid Reservoir

Battery

Engine Oil Dipstick

Washer Fluid Reservoir

Engine Oil Fill

Integrated Power Module (fuses)

Automatic Transmission Dipstick

Power Steering Fluid Reservoir – 2500/3500 Models Only

Air Cleaner Filter

Coolant Pressure Cap

Engine Coolant Reservoir

6.7L DIESEL ENGINE – 2500/3500 68RFE TRANSMISSION – IF EQUIPPED

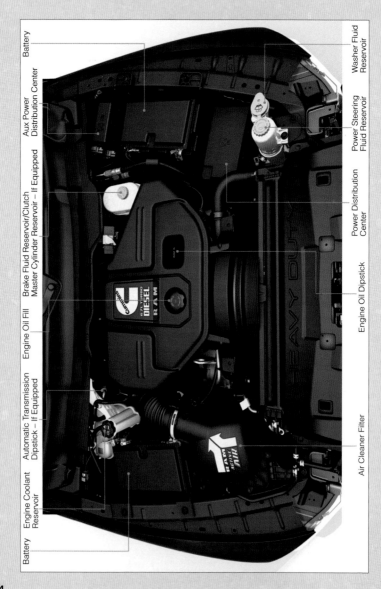

Battery

Engine Coolant Reservoir

Automatic Transmission Dipstick – If Equipped

Engine Oil Fill

Brake Fluid Reservoir/Clutch Master Cylinder Reservoir – If Equipped

Aux Power Distribution Center

Battery

Washer Fluid Reservoir

Power Steering Fluid Reservoir

Power Distribution Center

Engine Oil Dipstick

Air Cleaner Filter

6.7L DIESEL ENGINE – 3500 AS68RC HD TRANSMISSION – IF EQUIPPED

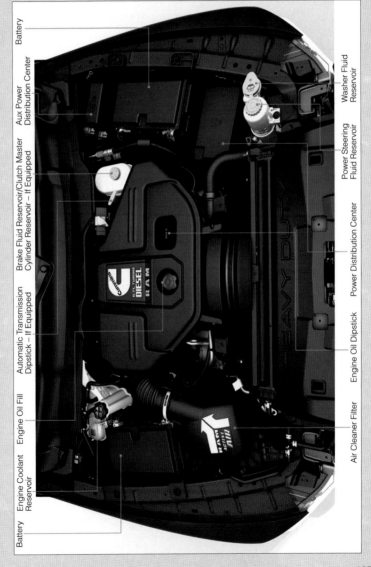

Battery | Engine Coolant Reservoir | Engine Oil Fill | Automatic Transmission Dipstick – If Equipped | Brake Fluid Reservoir/Clutch Master Cylinder Reservoir – If Equipped | Aux Power Distribution Center | Battery | Power Steering Fluid Reservoir | Washer Fluid Reservoir | Air Cleaner Filter | Engine Oil Dipstick | Power Distribution Center

MAINTAINING YOUR VEHICLE

FLUIDS AND CAPACITIES

Gasoline Versions

Component	Fluid, Lubricant, or Genuine Part	Capacities
Engine Coolant 3.6L, 4.7L Engine	We recommend you use MOPAR® Antifreeze/ Coolant 10 Year/150,000 Mile Formula OAT (Organic Additive Technology).	14 Quarts (13 Liters)
Engine Coolant 5.7L 1500 Models	We recommend you use MOPAR® Antifreeze/ Coolant 10 Year/150,000 Mile Formula OAT (Organic Additive Technology).	16 Quarts (15 Liters)
Engine Coolant 5.7L 2500/3500 Models	We recommend you use MOPAR® Antifreeze/ Coolant 10 Year/150,000 Mile Formula OAT (Organic Additive Technology) .	18.7 Quarts (17.7 Liters)
Engine Coolant 5.7L 2500/3500 Models w/Heavy Duty	We recommend you use MOPAR® Antifreeze/ Coolant 10 Year/150,000 Mile Formula OAT (Organic Additive Technology) .	19.2 Quarts (18.2 Liters)
Engine Oil with Filter 3.6L, 4.7L, 5.7L	We recommend you use API certified 5W-20 engine oil, meeting the requirements of Chrysler Material Standard MS-6395. Refer to you oil filler cap for correct SAE grade.	3.6L Engine - 6 Quarts (5.7 Liters) 4.7L Engine - 6 Quarts (5.7 Liters) 5.7L Engine - 7 Quarts (6.6 Liters)
Engine Oil with Filter 5.7L For 2500/3500 trucks operating with a gross combined weight rating greater than 14,000 lbs/(6,350 kg)	We recommend you use API Certified SAE 5W-30 engine oil, meeting the requirements of Chrysler Material Standard MS-6395. Refer to your engine oil filter cap for correct SAE grade.	5.7L Engine - 7 Quarts (6.6 Liters)
Engine Oil Filter 3.6L, 4.7L, 5.7L	We recommend you use MOPAR® Engine Oil Filters.	—
Spark Plug 3.6L	We recommend you use MOPAR® Spark Plugs.	—
Spark Plug 4.7L	We recommend you use MOPAR® Spark Plugs.	—
Spark Plug 5.7L	We recommend you use MOPAR® Spark Plugs.	—

Component	Fluid, Lubricant, or Genuine Part	Capacities
Automatic Transmission — Eight-Speed Automatic	We recommend you use Mopar® ZF 8&9 Speed ATF™ Automatic Transmission Fluid.	—
Automatic Transmission — Six-Speed Automatic with Gasoline Engine	We recommend you use MOPAR® ATF+4 Automatic Transmission Fluid.	—
Manual Transmission G-56	We recommend you use MOPAR® ATF+4 Automatic Transmission Fluid.	—
Transfer Case	We recommend you use MOPAR® ATF+4 Automatic Transmission Fluid.	—
Transfer Case – BW44–44 Only	We recommend you use MOPAR® BW44–44 Transfer Case Fluid.	—
Front Axle 1500 Four-Wheel Drive Models	We recommend you use GL-5 SAE 75W-90 MS-9763.	—
Rear Axle 1500 Models	We recommend you use MOPAR® Synthetic Gear Lubricant SAE 75W-140 MS-8985. Limited-Slip Rear Axles require the addition of 118 ml (4 oz) of MOPAR® Limited Slip Additive MS-10111.	—
Front and Rear Axle 2500/3500 Models	We recommend you use Synthetic, GL-5 SAE 75W-90. Limited-Slip 10.5/11.5 inch Rear Axles Limited slip additive is not required.	—
Brake Master Cylinder	We recommend you use MOPAR® DOT 3 and SAE J1703. If DOT 3 is not available, then DOT 4 is acceptable.	—
Power Steering Reservoir	We recommend you use MOPAR® Power Steering Fluid +4 or MOPAR® ATF+4® Automatic Transmission Fluid.	—

Component	Fluid, Lubricant, or Genuine Part	Capacities
Fuel Selection 3.6L, 4.7L	87 Octane	1500 Regular Cab Shortbed/Crew Quad Cab - 26 Gallons (98 Liters) (Approximate) 1500 Regular Cab Longbed/Crew Quad Cab (Optional) - 32 Gallons (121 Liters) (Approximate) 2500/3500 Shortbed - 34 Gallons (129 Liters) (Approximate) 2500/3500 Longbed - 35 Gallons (132 Liters) (Approximate)
Fuel Selection 5.7L	87 Octane Acceptable. 89 Octane Recommended.	1500 Regular Cab Shortbed/Crew Quad Cab - 26 Gallons (98 Liters) (Approximate) 1500 Regular Cab Longbed/Crew Quad Cab (Optional) - 32 Gallons (121 Liters) (Approximate) 2500/3500 Shortbed - 34 Gallons (129 Liters) (Approximate) 2500/3500 Longbed - 35 Gallons (132 Liters) (Approximate)

MAINTAINING YOUR VEHICLE

Diesel Versions

Component	Fluid, Lubricant, or Genuine Part	Capacities
Engine Coolant 6.7L Turbo Diesel Engine	We recommend you use MOPAR® Antifreeze/Coolant Ten Year/150,000 Mile Formula OAT (Organic Additive Technology).	5.7 Gallons (21.4 Liters)
Engine Oil with Filter 6.7L Turbo Diesel Engine	In ambient temperatures below 0°F (-18°C), We recommend you use 5W-40 synthetic engine oil that meets Chrysler Materials Standard MS-10902 and the API CJ-4 engine oil category is required. In ambient temperatures above 0°F (-18°C), We recommend you use 15W-40 engine oil that meets Chrysler Materials Standard MS-10902 and the API CJ-4 engine oil category is required.	12 Quarts (11.4 Liters)
Fuel Selection 6.7L Turbo Diesel	Use good quality diesel fuel from a reputable supplier in your vehicle. Federal law requires that you must fuel this vehicle with Ultra Low Sulfur Highway Diesel fuel (15 ppm Sulfur maximum) and prohibits the use of Low Sulfur Highway Diesel fuel (500 ppm Sulfur maximum) to avoid damage to the emissions control system. For most year-round service, No. 2 diesel fuel meeting ASTM specification D-975 Grade S15 will provide good performance. If the vehicle is exposed to extreme cold (below 20°F or -7°C), or is required to operate at colder-than-normal conditions for prolonged periods, use climatized No. 2 diesel fuel or dilute the No. 2 diesel fuel with 50% No. 1 diesel fuel. This will provide better protection from fuel gelling or wax-plugging of the fuel filters. This vehicle is fully compatible with biodiesel blends up to 5% biodiesel meeting ASTM specification D-975.	Standard Rear Tank - 52 Gallons (197 Liters) Optional Midship Tank - 22 Gallons (83 Liters)
Engine Oil Filter 6.7L Engine	We recommend you use MOPAR® Engine Oil Filters.	—
Engine Fuel Filter 6.7L Turbo Diesel	We recommend you use MOPAR® Fuel Filter. Must meet 5 micron rating. Using a fuel filter that does not meet the manufacturer's filtration and water separating requirements can severely impact fuel system life and reliability.	—
Crankcase Ventilation Filter 6.7L Turbo Diesel	We recommend you use MOPAR® CCV Filter.	—

Component	Fluid, Lubricant, or Genuine Part	Capacities
Automatic Transmission (5-Speed 545RFE)	MOPAR® ATF+4® Automatic Transmission Fluid or equivalent licensed ATF+4® product.	—
Automatic Transmission (6-Speed AS68RC)	MOPAR® AS68RC Automatic Transmission Fluid or equivalent.	
Clutch Linkage	We recommend you use MOPAR® Multi-Purpose Grease, NLGI Grade 2 E.P.	—
Manual Transmission G-56	We recommend you use MOPAR® ATF+4® Automatic Transmission Fluid.	—
Transfer Case	We recommend you use MOPAR® ATF+4® Automatic Transmission Fluid.	—
Transfer Case NVG 246 Only	We recommend you use MOPAR® NVG 246 Automatic Transmission Fluid.	—
Front and Rear Axle	We recommend you use We recommend you useSynthetic, GL-5 SAE, 75W-90 Synthetic (MS-9763) .	—
Brake Master Cylinder	We recommend you use MOPAR® DOT 3. If DOT 3 is not available, then DOT 4 is acceptable. Use only recommended Brake Fluids.	—
Power Steering Reservoir	We recommend you use MOPAR® Power Steering Fluid +4 or MOPAR® ATF+4® Automatic Transmission Fluid.	—
Diesel Exhaust Fluid Tank (Approximate)	We recommend you use MOPAR® Diesel Exhaust Fluid (API Certified) (DEF) or equivalent that has been API Certified to the ISO 22241 standard. Use of fluids not API Certified to ISO 22241 may result in system damage.	8 Gallons (30 Liters)

CAUTION!

- Mixing of engine coolant (antifreeze) other than specified Organic Additive Technology (OAT) engine coolant (antifreeze), may result in engine damage and may decrease corrosion protection. Organic Additive Technology (OAT) engine coolant is different and should not be mixed with Hybrid Organic Additive Technology (HOAT) engine coolant (antifreeze) or any "globally compatible" coolant (antifreeze). If a non-OAT engine coolant (antifreeze) is introduced into the cooling system in an emergency, it should be flushed with OAT coolant and replaced with the specified OAT engine coolant (antifreeze) as soon as possible.
- Do not use water alone or alcohol-based engine coolant (antifreeze) products. Do not use additional rust inhibitors or antirust products, as they may not be compatible with the radiator engine coolant and may plug the radiator.
- This vehicle has not been designed for use with propylene glycol-based engine coolant (antifreeze). Use of propylene glycol-based engine coolant (antifreeze) is not recommended.

E-85 Flexible Fuel – 4.7L Engine Only

CAUTION!

Only vehicles with the E-85 fuel filler door label or a yellow gas cap can operate on E-85.

Refer to your Owner's Manual on the DVD for further details.

MAINTENANCE SCHEDULE – GASOLINE ENGINE

Your vehicle is equipped with an automatic oil change indicator system. The oil change indicator system will remind you that it is time to take your vehicle in for scheduled maintenance.

Based on engine operation conditions, the oil change indicator message will illuminate. This means that service is required for your vehicle. Operating conditions such as frequent short-trips, trailer tow, extremely hot or cold ambient temperatures, and E85 fuel usage will influence when the "Oil Change Required" message is displayed. Severe Operating Conditions can cause the change oil message to illuminate as early as 3,500 miles (5,600 km) since last reset. Have your vehicle serviced as soon as possible, within the next 500 miles (805 km).

Your authorized dealer will reset the oil change indicator message after completing the scheduled oil change. If a scheduled oil change is performed by someone other than your authorized dealer, the message can be reset by referring to the steps described under "Electronic Vehicle Information Center (EVIC)/Oil Change Required" in "Understanding Your Instrument Panel" for further information.

MAINTAINING YOUR VEHICLE

NOTE:

Under no circumstances should oil change intervals exceed 10,000 miles (16,000 km) or twelve months, whichever comes first.

Once A Month Or Before A Long Trip:

• Check engine oil level

• Check windshield washer fluid level

• Check the tire inflation pressures and look for unusual wear or damage

• Check the fluid levels of the coolant reservoir, brake master cylinder, power steering (2500/3500 Models Only) and transmission as needed

• Check function of all interior and exterior lights

Required Maintenance

Refer to the Maintenance Schedules on the following pages for required maintenance.

At Every Oil Change Interval As Indicated By Oil Change Indicator System:
• Change oil and filter.
• Rotate the tires. **Rotate at the first sign of irregular wear, even if it occurs before the oil indicator system turns on.**
• Inspect battery and clean and tighten terminals as required.
• Inspect automatic transmission fluid if equipped with dipstick.
• Inspect brake pads, shoes, rotors, drums, hoses and park brake.
• Inspect engine cooling system protection and hoses.
• Inspect exhaust system.
• Inspect engine air cleaner if using in dusty or off-road conditions.
• Lube the front drive shaft fitting (2500/3500 (4x4) models only).

Maintenance Chart – Gasoline Engine

Mileage or time passed (whichever comes first)	20,000	30,000	40,000	50,000	60,000	70,000	80,000	90,000	100,000	110,000	120,000	130,000	140,000	150,000
Or Years:	2	3	4	5	6	7	8	9	10	11	12	13	14	15
Or Kilometers:	32,000	48,000	64,000	80,000	96,000	112,000	128,000	144,000	160,000	176,000	192,000	208,000	224,000	240,000
Additional Inspections														
Inspect the CV joints.	X							X						X
Inspect front suspension, tie rod ends, and replace if necessary.			X		X		X		X		X		X	
Inspect the front and rear axle surfaces. If gear oil leakage is suspected, check the fluid level. If using your vehicle for police, taxi, fleet, off-road or frequent trailer towing, change axle fluid.	X		X		X		X		X		X		X	
Inspect the brake linings, parking brake function.	X		X		X		X		X		X		X	
Inspect transfer case fluid.		X						X						X
Additional Maintenance														
Replace engine air filter.		X			X			X			X			X
Replace spark plugs (3.6L engine).**									X					
Replace the top row of spark plugs (4.7L Engine).**		X			X			X			X			X
Replace the top row and side row of spark plugs (4.7L Engine).**									X					
Replace spark plugs (5.7L engine).**					X			X			X			X
Replace the ignition cables (4.7L Engine).									X					
Flush and replace the engine coolant at 10 years or 150,000 miles (240,000 km) whichever comes first.									X					X
Change automatic transmission fluid and filter(s), if using your vehicle for police, taxi, fleet, or frequent trailer towing.					X									
Change automatic transmission fluid and filter.											X			

Mileage or time passed (whichever comes first)														
Or Years:	2	3	4	5	6	7	8	9	10	11	12	13	14	15
	20,000	30,000	40,000	50,000	60,000	70,000	80,000	90,000	100,000	110,000	120,000	130,000	140,000	150,000
Or Kilometers:	32,000	48,000	64,000	80,000	96,000	112,000	128,000	144,000	160,000	176,000	192,000	208,000	224,000	240,000
Inspect the transfer case fluid, change for any of the following: police, taxi, fleet, or frequent trailer towing.					X									
Change the transfer case fluid.									X		X			
Inspect and replace PCV valve if necessary.											X			

** The spark plug change interval is mileage based only, yearly intervals do not apply.

WARNING!

- You can be badly injured working on or around a motor vehicle. Do only service work for which you have the knowledge and the right equipment. If you have any doubt about your ability to perform a service job, take your vehicle to a competent mechanic.
- Failure to properly inspect and maintain your vehicle could result in a component malfunction and effect vehicle handling and performance. This could cause an accident.

MAINTAINING YOUR VEHICLE

MAINTENANCE RECORD

	Odometer	Date	Signature, Authorized Service Center
20,000 Miles (32,000 km) or 2 Years			
30,000 Miles (48,000 km) or 3 Years			
40,000 Miles (64,000 km) or 4 Years			
50,000 Miles (80,000 km) or 5 Years			
60,000 Miles (96,000 km) or 6 Years			
70,000 Miles (112,000 km) or 7 Years			
80,000 Miles (128,000 km) or 8 Years			
90,000 Miles (144,000 km) or 9 Years			
100,000 Miles (160,000 km) or 10 Years			
110,000 Miles (176,000 km) or 11 Years			
120,000 Miles (192,000 km) or 12 Years			
130,000 Miles (208,000 km) or 13 Years			
140,000 Miles (224,000 km) or 14 Years			
150,000 Miles (240,000 km) or 15 Years			

MAINTAINING YOUR VEHICLE

MAINTENANCE SCHEDULE – DIESEL ENGINE

CAUTION!
Failure to perform the required maintenance items may result in damage to the vehicle.

At Each Stop For Fuel

- Check the engine oil level at least 30 minutes after a fully warmed engine is shut off. Checking the oil level while the vehicle is on level ground will improve the accuracy of the oil level reading. Add oil only when the level is at or below the ADD or MIN mark.

Once A Month

- Inspect the batteries, and clean and tighten the terminals as required.
- Check the fluid levels of the coolant reservoir, brake master cylinder, and automatic transmission (if equipped), and add as needed.

At Each Oil Change

- Change the engine oil filter.
- Inspect the exhaust system.
- Check the coolant level, hoses, and clamps.
- Lubricate outer tie rod ends.

Inspection and service should also be performed anytime a malfunction is observed or suspected. Retain all receipts.

Oil Change Indicator System

Your vehicle is equipped with an engine oil change indicator system. This system will alert you when it is time to change your engine oil by displaying the words "Oil Change Due" on your Electronic Vehicle Information Center (EVIC). The engine oil change indicator system is duty cycle based, which means the engine oil change interval may fluctuate depending on your personal driving style. Driving styles such as frequent stop and go type driving or extended idle time can increase the frequency of the engine oil change. This is the result of more frequent regeneration of the exhaust after treatment system, which can decrease the life of the engine oil. Failure to change the engine oil per the maintenance schedule can result in internal engine damage.

For information on resetting the Oil Change Indicator message, refer to "Oil Change Due" under "Electronic Vehicle Information Center (EVIC)/EVIC Warning Lights" in "Understanding Your Instrument Panel" for further information.

Replace the engine oil and oil filter every 15,000 miles (24 000 km) or six months, or sooner if prompted by the oil change indicator system. Under no circumstances should oil change intervals exceed 15,000 miles (24 000 km) or six months, whichever comes first.

NOTE:

- **Under no circumstances should oil change intervals exceed 15,000 miles (24,000 km) or six months or 500 Hours, whichever comes first.**

- Replace the engine oil and oil filter every 12,500 miles (20 000 km) when running B20 fuel (Chassis Cab Only).

Perform Service Indicator

Your vehicle will require emissions maintenance at a set interval. To help remind you when this maintenance is due, the Electronic Vehicle Information Center (EVIC) will display "Perform Service". When the "Perform Service" message is displayed on the EVIC it is necessary to have the emissions maintenance performed. Emissions maintenance may include replacing the Closed Crankcase Ventilation (CCV) filter element. The procedure for clearing and resetting the "Perform Service" indicator message is located in the appropriate Service Information.

Maintenance Chart – Diesel Engine

Miles:	7,500	15,000	22,500	30,000	37,500	45,000	52,500	60,000	67,500	75,000	82,500	90,000	97,500
Or Months:	6	12	18	24	30	36	42	48	54	60	66	72	78
Or Kilometers:	12,000	24,000	36,000	48,000	60,000	72,000	84,000	96,000	108,000	120,000	132,000	144,000	156,000
Rotate the tires.	X	X	X	X	X	X	X	X	X	X	X	X	X
Lubricate front drive shaft fitting (4x4).	X	X	X	X	X	X	X	X	X	X	X	X	X
Lubricate outer tie rod ends.	X	X	X	X	X	X	X	X	X	X	X	X	X
Replace engine fuel filter element.		X		X		X		X		X		X	
Replace chassis mounted fuel filter element.		X		X		X		X		X		X	
Inspect the brake linings.			X			X			X			X	
Inspect and adjust parking brake.			X			X			X			X	
Inspect the front and rear axle surfaces. If gear oil leakage is suspected, check the fluid level. If using your vehicle for police, taxi, fleet, off-road or frequent trailer towing change the axle fluid.		X		X		X		X		X		X	
Inspect drive belt; replace as required.			X			X			X			X	
Check the transfer case fluid (4x4).				X				X				X	
Change the transfer case fluid (4x4).								X					
Inspect the front suspension, tie rod ends and boot seals for cracks or leaks and all parts for damage, wear, improper looseness or end play; replace if necessary.		X		X		X		X		X		X	
Inspect wheel bearings.				X				X				X	
Change automatic transmission fluid (AS69RC transmission only).								X				X	
Change automatic transmission fluid and filter(s) if using your vehicle for any of the following: police, fleet, or frequent trailer towing (68RFE transmission only).								X					

Miles:	7,500	15,000	22,500	30,000	37,500	45,000	52,500	60,000	67,500	75,000	82,500	90,000	97,500
Or Months:	6	12	18	24	30	36	42	48	54	60	66	72	78
Or Kilometers:	12,000	24,000	36,000	48,000	60,000	72,000	84,000	96,000	108,000	120,000	132,000	144,000	156,000
Change the manual transmission fluid if using your vehicle for any of the following: police, fleet, or frequent trailer towing.								X					
Check the Diesel Exhaust Fluid (DEF) tank; refill if necessary.	X	X	X	X	X	X	X	X	X	X	X	X	X
Replace Crankcase Ventilation Filter (CCV).									X				
Flush and replace power steering fluid.													X

MAINTAINING YOUR VEHICLE

Maintenance Record (Diesel Engine)

	Odometer	Date	Signature, Authorized Service Center
7,500 Miles (12,000 km) or 6 Months			
15,000 Miles (24,000 km) or 12 Months			
22,500 Miles (36,000 km) or 18 Months			
30,000 Miles (48,000 km) or 24 Months			
37,500 Miles (60,000 km) or 30 Months			
45,000 Miles (72,000 km) or 36 Months			
52,500 Miles (84,000 km) or 42 Months			
60,000 Miles (96,000 km) or 48 Months			
67,500 Miles (108,000 km) or 54 Months			
75,000 Miles (120,000 km) or 60 Months			
82,500 Miles (132,000 km) or 66 Months			
90,000 Miles (144,000 km) or 72 Months			
97,500 Miles (156,000 km) or 78 Months			

FUSES

POWER DISTRIBUTION CENTER (FUSES)

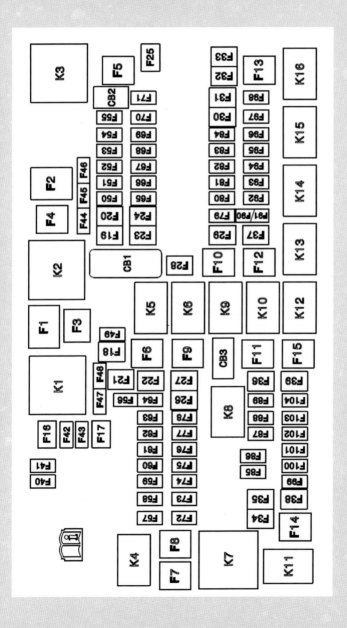

MAINTAINING YOUR VEHICLE

- The Power Distribution Center is located in the engine compartment near the battery. This center contains cartridge fuses and mini fuses. A description of each fuse and component may be stamped on the inside cover, otherwise the cavity number of each fuse is stamped on the inside cover that corresponds to the following chart.

Cavity	Cartridge Fuse	Micro Fuse	Description
F01	80 Amp Red		Rad Fan Control Module – If equipped
F03	60 Amp Yellow		Rad Fan – If Equipped
F05	40 Amp Green		Compressor for Air Suspension – If Equipped
F06	40 Amp Green		Antilock Brakes/Electronic Stability Control Pump
F07	40 Amp Green		Starter Solenoid
F08	40 Amp Green		Emissions Diesel – If Equipped
F09	40 Amp Green		Diesel Fuel Heater – If Equipped
F10	40 Amp Green		Body Controller / Exterior Lighting #2
F10	50 Amp Red		Body Controller / Exterior Lighting #2 – If Equipped with Stop/Start
F11	30 Amp Pink		Integrated Trailer Brake Module – If Equipped
F12	40 Amp Green		Body Controller #3 / Interior Lights
F13	40 Amp Green		Blower Motor
F14	40 Amp Green		Body Controller #4 / Power Locks
F15	30 Amp Pink		Electric Park Brake Right Side – If Equipped
F19	30 Amp Pink		SCR – If Equipped
F20	30 Amp Pink		Passenger Door Module
F21	30 Amp Pink		Drive Train Control Module
F22	20 Amp Yellow		Engine Control Module
F23	30 Amp Pink		Body Controller #1
F24	30 Amp Pink		Driver Door Module
F25	30 Amp Pink		Front Wiper Low Speed
F25	30 Amp Pink		Front Wiper High Speed
F26	30 Amp Pink		Antilock Brakes/Stability Control Module/Valves
F28	20 Amp Yellow		Trailer Tow Backup Lights – If Equipped
F29	20 Amp Yellow		Trailer Tow Parking Lights – If Equipped

Cavity	Cartridge Fuse	Micro Fuse	Description
F30	30 Amp Pink		Trailer Tow Receptacle
F32	30 Amp Pink		Drive Train Control Module – If Equipped
F33	20 Amp Yellow		Diesel Fuel Heater #1 – If Equipped / Rear Blower – If Equipped
F34	30 Amp Pink		Vehicle System Interface Module #2 – If Equipped
F35	30 Amp Pink		Sunroof – If Equipped
F36	30 Amp Pink		Rear Defroster– If Equipped
F37	30 Amp Pink		Diesel Fuel Heater #2 if equipped
F38	30 Amp Pink		Power Inverter 115V AC– If Equipped
F39	30 Amp Pink		Vehicle System Interface Module #1– If Equipped
F41		10 Amp Red	Active Grill Shutter
F42		20 Amp Yellow	Horn
F43		10 Amp Red	Snow Plow (Left) – If Equipped
F44		10 Amp Red	Diagnostic Port
F46		10 Amp Red	Tire Pressure Monitor
F47		10 Amp Red	Snow Plow (Right) – If Equipped
F49		10 Amp Red	Instrument Panel Cluster
F50		20 Amp Yellow	Air Suspension Control Module – If Equipped
F51		10 Amp Red	Ignition Node Module / Keyless Ignition
F52		5 Amp Tan	Battery Sensor
F53		20 Amp Yellow	Trailer Tow – Left Turn/Stop Lights
F54		20 Amp Yellow	Adjustable Pedals
F55		20 Amp Yellow	E38 Radio – If Equipped
F56		15 Amp Blue	Additional Diesel Content – If Equipped
F57		20 Amp Yellow	Transmission
F58		20 Amp Yellow (Gas Engine) / 25 Amp Natural (Diesel Engine)	Engine Cooling Pump
F60		15 Amp Blue	Underhood Lamp
F61		20 Amp Yellow	Power Take-off Unit – If Equipped

Cavity	Cartridge Fuse	Micro Fuse	Description
F62		10 Amp Red	Air Conditioning Clutch
F63		20 Amp Yellow	IgnitionCoils (Gas), Urea Heater (Diesel)
F64		25 Amp Natural	Fuel Injectors / Powertrain
F65		10 Amp Red	USB interface
F66		10 Amp Red	Sunroof / Passenger Window Switches / Rain Sensor
F67		10 Amp Red	CD / DVD / Bluetooth Hands-free Module – If Equipped
F69		15 Amp Blue	Mod SCR 12V – If Equipped
F70		30 Amp Green	Fuel Pump Motor
F71		25 Amp Natural	Amplifier
F72		10 Amp Red	Voltage Stabilizer Modules – If Equipped
F74		20 Amp Yellow (Gas Engine) / 10 Amp Red (Diesel Engine)	Brake Vacuum Pump Gas/Diesel – If Equipped
F75		10 Amp Red	Coolant Temperature Valve Actuator
F76		10 Amp Red	Antilock Brakes/Electronic Stability Control
F77		10 Amp Red	Drivetrain Control Module/Front Axle Disconnect Module
F78		10 Amp Red	Engine Control Module / Electric Power Steering
F79		15 Amp Blue	Clearance Lights
F80		10 Amp Red	Universal Garage Door Opener / Compass
F81		20 Amp Yellow	Trailer Tow Right Turn/Stop Lights
F82		10 Amp Red	Steering Column Control Module/ Cruise Control
F84		15 Amp Blue	Switch Bank/Instrument Cluster
F85		10 Amp Red	Airbag Module
F86		10 Amp Red	Airbag Module
F87		10 Amp Red	Air Suspension / Trailer Tow / Steering Column Control Module
F88		15 Amp Blue	Instrument Panel Cluster
F90/F91		20 Amp Yellow	Power Outlet (Rear seats) Customer Selectable

Cavity	Cartridge Fuse	Micro Fuse	Description
F93		20 Amp Yellow	Cigar Lighter
F94		10 Amp Red	Shifter / Transfer Case Module
F95		10 Amp Red	Rear Camera / Park Assist
F96		10 Amp Red	Rear Seat Heater Switch
F97		25 Amp Natural	Rear Heated Seats & Heated Steering Wheel – If Equipped
F98		25 Amp Natural	Front Heated Seats – If Equipped
F99		10 Amp Red	Climate Control
F101		15 Amp Blue	Electrochromatic Mirror / Smart High Beams – If Equipped
F104		20 Amp Yellow	Power Outlets (Instrument Panel/Center Console)

CAUTION!

• When installing the power distribution center cover, it is important to ensure the cover is properly positioned and fully latched. Failure to do so may allow water to get into the power distribution center and possibly result in an electrical system failure.

• When replacing a blown fuse, it is important to use only a fuse having the correct amperage rating. The use of a fuse with a rating other than indicated may result in a dangerous electrical system overload. If a properly rated fuse continues to blow, it indicates a problem in the circuit that must be corrected.

TIRE PRESSURES

• Check the inflation pressure of each tire, including the spare tire, at least monthly and inflate to the recommended pressure for your vehicle.

• The tire pressures recommended for your vehicle are found on the "Tire and Loading Information" label located on the driver's side door opening.

NOTE:
Refer to the Owner's Manual on the DVD for more information regarding tire warnings and instructions.

MAINTAINING YOUR VEHICLE

WARNING!

- Overloading of your tires is dangerous. Overloading can cause tire failure, affect vehicle handling, and increase your stopping distance. Use tires of the recommended load capacity for your vehicle. Never overload them.
- Improperly inflated tires are dangerous and can cause collisions. Under-inflation is the leading cause of tire failure and may result in severe cracking, component separation, or "blow out". Over-inflation reduces a tire's ability to cushion shock. Objects on the road and chuck holes can cause damage that results in tire failure. Unequal tire pressures can cause steering problems. You could lose control of your vehicle. Over-inflated or under-inflated tires can affect vehicle handling and can fail suddenly, resulting in loss of vehicle control.

WHEEL AND WHEEL TRIM CARE

- All wheels and wheel trim, especially aluminum and chrome plated wheels, should be cleaned regularly with a mild soap and water to prevent corrosion.
- To remove heavy soil and/or excessive brake dust, use MOPAR® Wheel Cleaner or equivalent or select a non-abrasive, non-acidic cleaner.

CAUTION!

Do not use scouring pads, steel wool, a bristle brush, or metal polishes. Do not use oven cleaner. These products may damage the wheel's protective finish. Avoid automatic car washes that use acidic solutions or harsh brushes that may damage the wheel's protective finish. Only MOPAR® Wheel Cleaner or equivalent is recommended.

EXTERIOR BULBS

LIGHT BULBS – Exterior	Bulb Number
Base Quad Headlamp – Low Beam	H11
Base Quad Headlamp – High Beam	9005
Front Turn Signal Lamp (Base Quad Headlamp)	3157NA
Premium Bi Halogen Projector Headlamp - Low Beam	HIR2
Premium Bi Halogen Projector Headlamp - High Beam	9005
Front Turn Signal Lamp (Premium Headlamp)	LED (Serviced at Authorized Dealer)
Fog Lamp (Horizontal shape)	9145
Fog Lamp (Vertical shape)	9006
Center High Mounted Stop Lamp (CHMSL)	921
Rear Cargo Lamp	921
Cab Roof Marker Lamps	194NA
Base Rear Tail/Turn and Stop Lamp	3157K
Premium Rear Tail/Turn and Stop Lamp	LED (Serviced at Authorized Dealer)
Premium Backup Lamp	T20
Rear Lamp Bar ID Marker Lamp	194
Side Marker Lamps (Dual Rear Wheels)	194
Backup Lamp	921
Rear License Plate Lamp	194

CUSTOMER ASSISTANCE

CHRYSLER GROUP LLC CUSTOMER CENTER

P.O. Box 21–8004 Auburn Hills, MI 48321–8004 Phone: 1–866–726–4636

CHRYSLER CANADA INC. CUSTOMER CENTER

P.O. Box 1621 Windsor, Ontario N9A 4H6 Phone: 1–800–465–2001 (English)
Phone: 1–800–387–9983 (French)

ASSISTANCE FOR THE HEARING IMPAIRED

• To assist customers who have hearing difficulties, the manufacturer has installed special TDD (Telecommunication Devices for the Deaf) equipment at its customer center. Any hearing or speech impaired customer, who has access to a TDD or a conventional teletypewriter (TTY) in the United States, can communicate with the manufacturer by dialing 1–800–380–CHRY. Canadian residents with hearing difficulties that require assistance can use the special needs relay service offered by Bell Canada. For TTY teletypewriter users, dial 711 and for Voice callers, dial 1–800–855–0511 to connect with a Bell Relay Service operator.

WARNING!

Engine exhaust, some of its constituents, and certain vehicle components contain, or emit, chemicals known to the State of California to cause cancer and birth defects, or other reproductive harm. In addition, certain fluids contained in vehicles and certain products of component wear contain, or emit, chemicals known to the State of California to cause cancer and birth defects, or other reproductive harm.

PUBLICATIONS ORDERING

• **If you are the first registered retail owner of your vehicle,** you may obtain one free printed copy of the Owner's Manual, Warranty Booklet or Radio Manuals on your DVD by calling 1–866–726–4636 (U.S.) or 1–800–387–1143 (Canada) or by contacting your dealer.

• Replacement User Guide kits or DVDs or, if you prefer, additional printed copies of the Owner's Manual, Warranty Booklet or Radio Manuals may be purchased by visiting www.techauthority.com or by calling 1–800–890–4038 (U.S.) or 1–800–387–1143 (Canada). Visa, Master Card, American Express and Discover orders are accepted. If you prefer mailing your order, please call the above numbers for an order form.

NOTE:

• A street address is required when ordering manuals (no P.O. Boxes).

• The Owner's Manual and User Guide electronic files are also available on the Chrysler, Jeep, Ram Truck and Dodge websites.

- Click on the "For Owners" tab, select "Owner/Service Manuals", then select your desired model year and vehicle from the drop down lists.

REPORTING SAFETY DEFECTS IN THE 50 UNITED STATES AND WASHINGTON, D.C.

- If you believe that your vehicle has a defect that could cause a collision or cause injury or death, you should immediately inform the National Highway Traffic Safety Administration (NHTSA) in addition to notifying the manufacturer.

- If NHTSA receives similar complaints, it may open an investigation, and if it finds that a safety defect exists in a group of vehicles, it may order a recall and remedy campaign. However, NHTSA cannot become involved in individual problems between you, your authorized dealer and the manufacturer.

- To contact NHTSA, you may either call the Auto Safety Hotline toll free at 1–888–327–4236 (TTY: 1–800–424–9153), or go to http://www.safercar.gov; or write to: Administrator, NHTSA, 1200 New Jersey Avenue, SE., West Building, Washington, D.C. 20590. You can also obtain other information about motor vehicle safety from http://www.safercar.gov.

In Canada

- If you believe that your vehicle has a safety defect, you should contact the Customer Service Department immediately. Canadian customers who wish to report a safety defect to the Canadian government should contact Transport Canada, Motor Vehicle Defect Investigations and Recalls at 1-800-333-0510 or go to http://www.tc.gc.ca/eng/roadsafety/safedrivers-childsafety-index-53.htm

- French Canadian customers who wish to report a safety defect to the Canadian government should contact Transport Canada, Motor Vehicle Defect Investigations and Recalls at 1-800-333-0510 or go to http://www.tc.gc.ca/securiteroutiere/

MOPAR ACCESSORIES

AUTHENTIC ACCESSORIES BY MOPAR®

- The following highlights just some of the many Authentic Ram Truck Accessories by Mopar featuring a fit, finish, and functionality specifically for your Ram Truck.
- In choosing Authentic Accessories you gain far more than expressive style, premium protection, or extreme entertainment, you also benefit from enhancing your vehicle with accessories that have been thoroughly tested and factory-approved.
- For the full line of Authentic Ram Truck Accessories by Mopar, visit your local Ram Truck dealership or online at mopar.com.

CHROME:

- Exhaust Tip
- Chrome Cast Aluminum Wheels
- Tubular Side Steps
- Front Air Deflector
- Fuel Filler Door
- Grille

EXTERIOR:

- Under-The-Rail Bedliner
- Fiberglass Tonneau Cover
- Snapless Tonneau Cover
- Molded Splash Guards
- Running Boards
- Bed Extender
- Bed Step
- Hitch Receiver
- Fender Flares
- Bed Mat
- Tool Box
- Sports Performance Hood

INTERIOR:

- Premium Carpet Floor Mats
- Ambient Light Kit
- Door Sill Guards
- Bright Pedal Kit
- Slush Mats
- Heated Seats

ELECTRONICS:

- Kicker® Sound Systems
- Mopar Web
- Uconnect® 730N
- Head Restraint DVD Rear Seat Video
- Uconnect® 430/430N
- Sirius Satellite Radio
- DVD Rear Seat Video™

CARRIERS:

- Bed Mounted Bike Carrier
- Bed Mounted Ski and Snowboard Carrier
- Bed Mounted Cargo Basket With Cargo Net
- Cargo Bed Divider
- Cargo Ramps
- Diamond Plate Toolbox

- iPod® is a registered trademark of Apple, Inc.
- Kicker® is a registered trademark of Stillwater Designs and Audio, Inc.

INDEX

Adjustable Pedals 24
Airbag 14
Air Conditioning 33, 34, 36, 37
Air Suspension 31
Anti-Lock Brake System (ABS) . . .136
Arming Theft System (Security
    Alarm) 13
Automatic Headlights 26
Automatic Temperature Control
    (ATC) 36
Automatic Transmission
    Fluid Type 166
Axle Fluid 166

Back-Up Camera 38
Battery
    Charging System Light 136
Belts, Seat 13
Brake Fluid 166
Brake System
    Warning Light 136
Break-In Recommendations, New
    Vehicle 25
Bulb Replacement 187

Calibration, Compass. 102
Cargo Light 27
Change Oil Indicator 137
Charging System Light 136
Check Engine Light (Malfunction
    Indicator Light) 136
Child Restraint 15
Child Restraint Tether Anchors 15
Climate Control 33, 34, 36
Compass Calibration 102
Cooling System
    Coolant Capacity 166
Crankcase Emission Control
    System 27
Cruise Control (Speed Control) 27
Cruise Light. 28
Customer Assistance 188
Customer Programmable Features .102

Defects, Reporting 189
Defroster, Rear Window 33, 34
Defroster, Windshield 33, 34
Dimmer Control. 27

Disarming, Theft System 13
Driver Cockpit 6

Electronic Range Select (ERS). .29, 31
Electronics
    Your Vehicle's Sound System . .42
Electronic Speed Control (Cruise
    Control). 27
Electronic Throttle Control Warning
    Light 137
Electronic Vehicle Information Center
    (EVIC). 101
Emergency, In Case of
    Overheating 138
Engine
    Block Heater 124
    Break-In
    Recommendations 25, 124
    Compartment 161
    Malfunction Indicator (Check
    Engine) 136
    Oil Selection 166
    Overheating 138
    Starting 12
    Stopping 12
Event Data Recorder 159
Exhaust Brake. 125
Exterior Lights. 187

Flat Tire Stowage 149
Fluid Capacities. 166
Fluids 166
Fog Lights. 26
Freeing A Stuck Vehicle 158
Front Heated Seats. 22
Fuel
    Specifications 166
Fuse 181
Fuses. 181

Garage Door Opener (HomeLink®) .104

Headlight 26
Headlights
    Automatic 26
    Dimmer Switch 27
    High Beam 26
    Switch 26

191

INDEX

Heated Steering Wheel 23
Heater, Engine Block. 124
High Beam/Low Beam Select
   (Dimmer) Switch 26
HomeLink® (Garage Door Opener) .104
Hood Release 160
Hub Caps 147

Idle Up Feature 126
Integrated Trailer Brake Controls . .120
Intermittent Wipers (Delay Wipers) . .26
Introduction 3
Inverter Outlet (115V) 107
Inverter, Power 107

Jack Location 138
Jump Starting 152

Keyless Enter-N-Go 11
   Lock/Unlock 11
   Starting/Stopping 12

Lane Change and Turn Signals 26
Lane Change Assist 26
LATCH (Lower Anchors and Tether
   for CHildren). 15
Lights
   Turn Signal 26

Maintenance Record 175, 180
Maintenance Schedule .171, 176, 178
Malfunction Indicator Light (Check
   Engine). 136
Memory Seat 21
Message Center
   Water in Fuel 124
MOPAR® Accessories. 190

Navigation 71, 89
New Vehicle Break-In Period . .25, 124

Oil Change Indicator 137, 176
Oil Change Indicator, Reset 137
Oil, Engine
   Capacity 166
Outlet
   Power 108

Overheating, Engine 138

Park Sense System, Rear 37
Pedals, Adjustable 24
Perform Service Indicator, Reset . .177
Pickup Box 112
Placard, Tire and Loading
   Information. 185
Power
   Distribution Center (Fuses) . . .181
   Glass Sunroof 40
   Inverter 107
   Outlet (Auxiliary Electrical
     Outlet) 108
   Seats 20
   Sliding Rear Window 39
   Steering 166
Preparation for Jacking. 140
Programmable Electronic
   Features 102

Rain Sensitive Wiper System 26
Rear Camera 38
Rear Park Sense System 37, 38
Recreational Towing 121
Remote Starting System 12
Replacement Bulbs. 187
Reporting Safety Defects. 189
Resetting Perform Service
   Indicator 177

Schedule, Maintenance 171
Seat Belts 13
Seats. 20
   Heated 22
   Lumbar Support 20
   Memory 21
   Power 20
   Ventilated 22
Shift Lever Override 154
Signals, Turn 26
SIRIUS Travel Link 92
SmartBeams 27
Spark Plugs 166
Speed Control (Cruise Control) 27
Starting
   Cold Weather 125
   Remote 12

INDEX

Starting Procedures (Diesel
  Engines) 124
Sun Roof 40

Tailgate 112
Temperature Control, Automatic
  (ATC) 36
Theft System Arming. 13
Theft System Disarming 13
Tires
  Air Pressure 185
  Changing 141
  Flat Changing 141
  Jacking 141
  Pressure Monitor System
  (TPMS) 38
  Pressure Warning Light 134
Tow/Haul. 120
Tow Hooks, Emergency. 154
Towing
  Disabled Vehicle 157
  Recreational 121
Towing Vehicle Behind a
  Motorhome. 121

Trailer Towing
  Trailer and Tongue Weight . . .118
Transfer Case
  Fluid 166
Transmission
  Fluid 166
  Warning Light 137
Turn Signals. 26

Uconnect® 3.0 54
Uconnect® 5.0 57
Uconnect® 8.4A 63
Uconnect® 8.4AN 82

Ventilated Seats 22

Washers, Windshield 26
Water in Fuel 124
Wheel and Wheel Trim Care 186
Wheel Cover 147
Wheel Nut Torque. 148
Wind Buffeting 41
Windshield Washers 26
Windshield Wipers 26

FAQ (How To?)

FREQUENTLY ASKED QUESTIONS

GETTING STARTED

How do I install my LATCH Equipped Child Seat? pg. 15

How do I program my Front Seat Memory? pg. 21

OPERATING YOUR VEHICLE

How does the Electronic Range Select (ERS) operate? pg. 29

What do I do if my TPMS warning light is blinking? pg. 38

Where is the Tire Light Load Inflation switch located? pg. 38

ELECTRONICS

Which radio is in my vehicle?

- Uconnect® 3.0 pg. 54
- Uconnect® 5.0 pg. 57
- Uconnect® 8.4A pg. 63
- Uconnect® 8.4AN pg. 82

How do I activate the Audio Jack?

- Uconnect® 3.0 pg. 56
- Uconnect® 5.0 pg. 59
- Uconnect® 8.4A pg. 68
- Uconnect® 8.4AN pg. 68

How do I set the clock on my radio?

- Uconnect® 3.0 pg. 55
- Uconnect® 5.0 pg. 57
- Uconnect® 8.4A pg. 63
- Uconnect® 8.4AN pg. 82

How do I use the Navigation feature?

- Uconnect® 8.4A pg. 71
- Uconnect® 8.4AN pg. 89

How do I pair my cell phone via Bluetooth® with the Uconnect® Hands-Free Voice Activation System?

- Uconnect® 8.4A pg. 93
- Uconnect® 8.4AN pg. 93

How do I use my iPod®? pg. 68

How do I use my USB port to listen to audio through my touch-screen radio? pg. 68

FAQ (How To?)

OFF-ROAD CAPABILITIES

How do I shift into different four-wheel drive selections? pg. 109

UTILITY

How do I know how much I can tow with my Ram Truck? pg. 118

How do I adjust the gain on the Integrated Trailer Brake Module? pg. 120

WHAT TO DO IN EMERGENCIES

What do I do if my TPMS warning light is blinking? pg. 134

How do I change a flat tire? pg. 141

How do I Jump-Start my vehicle? pg. 152

MAINTAINING YOUR VEHICLE

Where is my Fuse Block located? pg. 181

What type of oil do I use? pg. 166

How often should I change my engine's oil?

- Gasoline Engine pg. 171
- Diesel Engine pg. 176

What should my tire pressure be set at? pg. 185

NOTES

NOTES